THOUGHT CATALOG BOOKS

Being Whole

Being Whole

All the Things I Never Told You, Or Admitted to Myself

LACEY RAMBURGER

THOUGHT CATALOG BOOKS

Brooklyn, NY

THOUGHT CATALOG BOOKS

Copyright © 2016 by Lacey Ramburger

All rights reserved. Published by Thought Catalog Books, a division of The Thought & Expression Co., Williamsburg, Brooklyn. Founded in 2010, Thought Catalog is a website and imprint dedicated to your ideas and stories. We publish fiction and non-fiction from emerging and established writers across all genres. For general information and submissions: manuscripts@thoughtcatalog.com.

First edition, 2016

ISBN 978-1945796203

10 9 8 7 6 5 4 3 2 1

Cover design by © KJ Parish

Contents

Part III. This is The One I Could Have Loved

Part IV. This Was Loving My Best Friend

Part V. This Is Loving Myself

Praise for "Being Whole"

In her debut collection, Ramburger examines her past with an unwavering vulnerability. She writes about past love, failed relationships, and promises to her future self in a way anyone who has given their heart away can relate to. Still so young in her career, Ramburger exhibits a raw talent at telling the truth and stripping away any false pretense in her work. It's a beautiful thing to be so willing to expose your rawest hurt, and Ramburger does it beautifully.

—Ari Eastman

Lacey Ramburgers's words will stay with you long after you have read them. In *Being Whole,* Lacey beautifully and eloquently tells the honest truth to her past lovers and to herself. While her words leave pangs in your heart and tears in your eyes, her words and poetry also sprout beauty and growth. Throughout her book, Lacey is painfully honest and you can't help but root for her and cheer her on. She stands tall and does not apologize for feeling the way that she does. And she never apologizes for being herself. Being a great writer is about being honest. Being a great writer is about telling your own personal truth. And Ramburger does just that with every word that she writes.

—Lauren Jarvis-Gibson

Acknowledgements

God, thank you for this life, for these people, and for all of Your love, mercy, and grace. Mom and Dad thank you for everything. Literally, every single thing. I love you more than words. Kaitlin, Sarah, Beckie, Dana, Samantha, Taylor, Madi, Cayla, and Hannah thank you for listening to all my stories and feelings for all these people for far too long. You're the best friends anyone could ask for. Kendra you're the most incredible producer, writer, and friend. Thank you for seeing great things in me, answering all of my questions, and being an absolutely beautiful human inside and out. Lauren, thank you for Loving Taylor Swift as much as I do, always embracing the feels, and being a genuine ray of sunshine in my life. You're incredible and wonderful. Thought Catalog, thank you for taking a chance on me, you've let me pursue dreams I didn't know I would ever achieve.

R, L, Z, and J – Thanks for the memories. If you didn't know, now you do.

Foreword

I am not an emotional girl.

I know. Even having the audacity to write that sentence kind of makes me a cliché, but bear with me.

In dealing with my own heartbreak that happened in my early 20s, my natural reaction was to repress, repress, repress. I never talked to him. I rarely talked about him. I resorted to eye rolls and some really morbid thoughts whenever he'd come up in passing. I refused to acknowledge my feelings and, even worse, refused to acknowledge that they were even valid in the first place.

And in doing so, there were so many things that I never said, and never admitted to myself.

Lacey, with her stunning words and startlingly confessional style, has done exactly the opposite.

Instead of repressing her pain, she's embraced it. Instead of ignoring her heartbreak, she's accepted it. Instead of pretending like her hurt, and subsequently the people who have hurt her, don't exist, she has acknowledged their validity in her life. Instead of running away from the things she should deal with, she's turned around to face them head on.

Instead of allowing herself to be broken, she's made an active choice to be whole.

When faced with the reality that someone we love might not love us back, we have a choice to make. We can resist the pain, we can ignore it, we can pretend like it doesn't exist. Or we can choose to love ourselves enough on our own instead.

And Lacey has clearly made the right choice.

Lacey Ramburger is the kind of writer that leaves an impact. Her words resonate and stick with you long after you've closed out the tab or set down the manuscript. She's the kind of writer who you find yourself turning to in times of joy, in times of pain, and in times when you just need a reminder that there is in fact a tomorrow.

Her own heartbreaks may have left her a changed woman, but it's a woman we all need in our lives. And it's a woman I'm so thankful I've found a place for in my own.

I am not an emotional girl. But Lacey still makes me feel things.

And I can promise that she will make you feel things as well. And in the end, you will absolutely be a little bit more complete (and more whole) than you were before she was around.

Kendra Syrdal – Producer at Thought Catalog

1

Beginnings

If anyone ever asked me what my dream was, it was very simple. I wanted to get married and share a future with the love of my life.

And by all accounts, it was you.

The first time I ever saw you, we were playing an intense game of Red Rover and you came barreling right towards me without knowing who I was. You definitely broke the chain link and slammed right into me, taking me down to the ground without the slightest pause to indicate I had slowed you down for even a second.

We would tell that story to people when they asked how we first met, and you would say you "knocked me off my feet."

You really did, and I would never be the same.

Despite that you were everything I ever wanted, I never believed I had a chance with you. You were older, already graduated from college, working a job that wasn't fast food or retail. I was 18, fresh out of high school, not even certain where I was going to college or what I wanted to do with my life. You were stable, kind, and reassuring. I was scattered, optimistic, and indecisive.

When you told me you had feelings for me, it didn't feel real. I couldn't understand what you saw in me. Yet you still looked at me the way every girl dreams of being looked at. The look that Disney has perfected, that look that silently whispers "I am so in love with you."

I looked at you and the only thing that felt certain was the quiet voice in my head saying, *You're going to marry him.* That was all I ever wanted. It was all I ever could've hoped for in my wildest dreams. And you did ask me to spend the rest of my life with you.

Yet darling, I learned that the path I always dreamed of was not the one I was destined to take.

At least not with you.

2

Perfect

There are things I never told anyone. Except you. One of those things is that I was the kind of girl who used to make "future husband" lists. The kind that listed all the attributes of the man I wanted to marry.

You were everything I ever could've dreamed of.

When I pictured the love of my life, the one I wanted to spend forever with, you were it to a T. You were kind; you were willing to do anything to help someone out, even when it put you in an inconvenient situation. You were intelligent; you built machines and knew all the ins and outs of technology that I never did. Your sense of humor consisting of puns and cheesy jokes kept me in stitches. You loved God, and you had a heart for teenagers that loved Him, too. You were a family man; your parents adored you and young cousins who looked up to you. And from the moment I fell in love, the only thing that rang clear in my mind is that I was going to marry you.

I was almost right.

I never told you this, but I never had loved someone the way I loved you. I would've blindly followed you to the ends of the earth. I would've packed my bags and moved anywhere. I would've stayed with you always; all you had to do was say so. All I ever wanted was to make you happy, even when it meant taking the parts of me that you deemed immature, embarrassing, and messy and trying to replace them with better things. I honestly would've done anything for you if you had simply loved me as much as I loved you. The way I loved you was consuming and you held every single piece of me in your hands.

And I will never love someone that way again. Not because they don't deserve a complete, wholehearted kind of love. But because that kind of love…it's not healthy. It's the kind of love that says, "I'll listen to you even if you're wrong. I'll do what you say even if it means changing everything I am. I'll be whatever you want me to be."

And darling, I'm not even sure if that's love.

3

Fairy Tale

Sometimes I think we were too much like a fairy tale.

Maybe that's a good thing; maybe it was our downfall. Yet I can remember our memories highlighted in shades of red and rose, and the pictures show two people madly in love who didn't think that one day they'd do anything but smile at each other.

I remember making a sunrise picnic for us and setting our alarms for an ungodly hour to be getting up for vacation. I had brought a blanket and spent the night before making us breakfast sandwiches and bought sparkling grape juice and little flutes to drink out of, being as overwhelmingly romantic as an 18 year old knew how. I snuck a card that I had bought for you, my own words filling the inside of it with how much I adored you and cherished this life we were building together. We watched the sunrise and we stared in awe, no words able to match the beauty of the skyline.

I remember us creating our own prom in my living room because my senior year I decided not to go. I was too busy crushing on you from afar and no one else interested me. I still had the dress I would've worn in the closet, so one summer night we both dressed up and danced around the coffee table in my living room to MuteMath and Taylor Swift and what-ever else felt like a soundtrack for this love we were starting.

I remember making a scavenger hunt for our first Valentine's Day, creating QR codes that you could scan with your phone to give you clues to the next place. I scattered them all through your apartment until you made it to the kitchen where you found your gifts and food for us to cook dinner that night. The apartment was small enough where you wouldn't have had to look very hard, but you went along with it because we made do with what we had and it was more than enough for us.

I remember the first Christmas together. I bought you a Christmas tree and had your mother unlock the apartment for me so that I could sneak it in. I took it out of its box and put it together. It was one piece of holiday spirit that you had said you wished you had. It was already set up when you came home from work, and your face lit up more than the tree did. You were overwhelmed that I would even think to do some-thing like that.

The truth is I went above and beyond in everything I did for you. I won't pretend you never did anything for me, because you did, and I remember them well. Yet I never thought twice about putting everything on the line for you. I never thought twice about doing all these over-the-top romantic things that just felt so natural. Because the way I loved you seemed just as natural as anything else I had ever done.

Sometimes I wish I still had that part of me, but I lost it when you left. I lost that desire to do those types of things, not because no one else deserved them, but because I realized you could love someone so much and do all of these things, and love can still die. So every time I think of doing something that requires a lot of planning, I think of you and those looks on your face that said you'd never forget those moments. I lost the part of me that can easily do all of those things for someone else without a second thought, and I wish you could've just left that part behind. I noticed you started doing over-the-top things for the one you loved next, though. So I guess you put that part to good use. At the very least, if I couldn't have it anymore, you didn't leave it dormant in the back of your mind. You didn't leave it to collect dust and decay. At least I know that though I don't hold that part anymore, it didn't die. One piece didn't die.

4

Losing Weight and Losing You

"You're all skin and bones."
That's what my mother told me.
I told her she's imagining things,
But I knew.

Trust me, I knew.

I'd been carrying the weight
of your expectations.
Carrying the weight of
"I'm not wife material."

Carrying it all on my shoulders,
carrying its symbol on my left hand.
Carrying so much of this weight,
that I was starting to lose my own.

I lost 19 pounds,
and I don't think you even noticed.
I'd almost say that's the reason you stopped
calling me beautiful,

but your eyes stopped looking at me
long before that happened.

5

If

You were the first one to really break me down.

The night we fought in the house; the night where we are arguing and you're tossing around phrases like "If we get married." Calling into question our relationship because of clothes on the bed and un-mopped floors. You probably didn't mean to do that, I know. I also know that you had never once said "if" when it came to us. My mind shot back to two years ago, before we were ever dating, lying in a hammock in the summer sun, and you said "*When* we get married…" I cut you off with "Don't say things you don't mean." Yet back then you smiled, telling me how it was still *when*. You believed in us as much as I did. You believed so much that you got down on one knee and placed a ring on my finger. Yet here we are 2 months after the wonderful proposal, and I'm hoping that "if" was a slip of the tongue, something said in anger and not something you adopted into your new frame of mind. Yet then there it is again…*if*. You say it three more times. "If… If…IF."

I've always hated that word.

So I feel the waterworks, the salt stinging my eyes, the seizing up of my throat, all at once silencing me and forcing me to open my mouth to let the sobs pour out. To let the embarrassment and the hurt pour out of me, trying to cleanse me from this *if*.

I tell you I'm going home, that I need to rest and we need to both have time to cool down, despite that I know I'll be up all night. I never told you that I pulled out of the driveway and drove around town, trying to hold back tears. I couldn't go to my apartment with a roommate who barely knew me, bawling and waking her up at 2 AM. I wasn't going to run to my parents, because if they saw my tears they would hate you. They'd hate anyone who broke me enough to make me cry. So I pull into an empty park and let the tears roll, let the sobs spill out of my mouth only asking "Why?"

That was the first time I cried over us, and I would continue to cry in the months to come. Maybe my heart already knew that night was the beginning of the end. Perhaps my heart decided to start mourning for us six months early because it knew it would take a long time to get you out of my system.

6

Part of Me

When a breakup happens, they don't tell you
That you lose pieces of you in the split.
It's not like a divorce, where you have
lawyers to draw up contracts that say
"This is mine, this is yours, this is what we share."

There are no terms,
no way to calculate what is fair
and what is equal.
No custody arrangement
for this pain we created.

Once two people who intertwined
themselves together come undone,
it isn't as simple as
untwisting and untangling limbs;
you realize that in the process
your souls stitched themselves together
when you were sharing stories and
learning the ways the other moved.

When you start pulling
in opposite directions,
you feel the rips, the threads shredding,
but nothing is equal.

You don't walk away with
all of you still together,
but you have parts of him
in your blood now,
and he has parts of you.
You can't get them back;
you can't demand that those things
be returned to their rightful owner:
You.

When we ended it all I lost one too many things.
If I could have gone back now,
I would've asked for them back,
tried to get them back.

I want my first kiss back.
I want back the part of me
who didn't know how
these things worked
and how it felt to be
made alive by someone else.

I want my ability to love
before being broken back.
The love I had for you
had never touched heartbreak,
never felt so much as a bruise,
it was the biggest amount
of love I could give.

I want back the part of me

that believed in forever and believed
that love only died when you
cheated, lied, or mistreated.
It may have been naïve,
but I wish I'd held onto it
for a little longer.

I just wish I could have held on to
the parts of me that you walked away with,
the parts of me that you still carry
in you somewhere despite that it may
have been forgotten about.
The parts that are in boxes,
stored away, the parts that
haven't seen light in years.

The parts of me that I could never replace.

7

Habits

Sometimes we convince ourselves
we need to go back.
That we somehow belong
in our old spaces a second time.

We don't like to admit it.
Let's avoid talking about our weakness.
Let's talk about our strength and maybe it will show up
and replace the aches from yesterday.

It's been over a month since
I gave you back the ring
and I say I'm fine.

Maybe if I keep saying it out loud
it will become true.
People seem to believe it;
you most certainly do.

When we end up at your doorstep,
perhaps I've tricked myself
into thinking I'm strong enough to go in.
Or maybe I miss you so much, I can't tell.

They say when you're in old habitats
with familiar faces,

your body doesn't
always break its habits.
We are the most familiar thing
I've ever known,
maybe that's why
your arms are around me.

"I don't want us to get confused."
You say, but
I'm not confused.
We are two puzzle pieces
not meant to fit,
but our mouths are still magnetic.

So we are pushing lips together,
trying to find the familiar groove
we perfected for two years.
It doesn't take us long.

I stay far longer than I should,
eventually we have to come back for air.
Yet now I'm finding it even harder to breathe,
everything starts to feel clear again.

I tell you I need to get out of here.
This air, it isn't oxygen.
Oxygen doesn't burn your lungs
or cause tears in your eyes.

I make my way out, stumbling to my car,
you walk me out because

it's what you've always done.
I sit in my car and start to form
the word "goodbye."
instead it bursts out of me.

"I love you."

We both stare at each other,
and I'm stumbling over words,
over apologies and explanations
hoping maybe you can just forget it happened.

"Hey, it's okay. I love you, too."
I look up and give a half smile.
Those words are the best
and worst words I could ever hear.

Because I can't get rid of my feelings over night,
and I know love doesn't simply die
in a day, week, or month.
Yet the biggest fear
I seem to have
is whether there will be a day
where I can ever stop.

8

Ready

I never told you that despite how I was the one to go on a date first, you were really the first one to move on.

In your eyes, and the rest of the world's eyes, I had been the one to move on first. I was the one who went on a date just one month after we broke up. I was the one who was anxious to meet new people, to get back out there—and make no mistake—I absolutely was ready. Just not in the way I needed to be. I wanted to move on. I wanted to get back out there, but that wasn't what I *needed*. I honestly and truly wasn't ready, but I didn't want to believe that. I wanted to not need you to be happy, to not let you define me, to not let us define me. I wanted a clean slate and a new association that didn't automatically include you.

So when I met that really attractive guy at the coffee shop and we struck up a conversation, I was excited. I wasn't thinking, *This will show him.* I was thinking, *Oh good. Someone that makes me smile. This is a good thing.* I didn't think twice about this being me "moving on," but here I was, trying to. Trying to allow myself to get off the ground and walk into a world that didn't include you and me anymore.

Yet I was nowhere near ready because I still wasn't over us. I hadn't recovered as well as I thought I had, because as I was walking down the riverfront with this interesting guy who makes me laugh and makes me think, I somehow manage to let spill from my mouth the fact that I was engaged a month ago. I brought you into my date when I swore up and down that I wasn't thinking about you. I immediately wished I could hide or run or someone rewind time and force my mouth closed, but my date didn't run. He seemed surprised, maybe thrown off guard, but he went with the flow. We changed subjects and acted like I'd never said a word about you.

Bringing you up wasn't what caused me and him to not work out, but it did cause me to realize that I truly wasn't over you. Or us. I knew I didn't want you back. I knew we weren't right for each other and we had established that. Yet I still wasn't healed. I had pieces scattered everywhere and I truly just wanted them to be put back together. What should've happened was that I took some time for me. I should've stepped back and said that I needed to let myself heal before I went back out into the dating world again.

That did not happen.

Instead I kept pushing forward, dragging my broken pieces behind me, hoping that eventually they would all just come back together the same way they did for you two months after my date. I kept thinking that eventually, things would just make sense, that I would be okay, and that someone else would be able to make their home in me again the way you had.

It was my fault for pretending I was okay when I wasn't. It was my fault for being so bitter because you didn't move on to hurt me. You didn't do it out of spite. You moved on because you found someone, a wonderful someone at that. It was my fault for holding everything in and not letting it come out until it forced itself to, until it demanded to be felt. It was easier to be angry at you, but if I'm honest, I was really angry at me.

9

"We're already a couple now, but I'm sure you knew that already."

Three months. That's all it took for you to heal.
Part of me is grateful but
I'm still recovering.

I'm still fighting off fears
in my sleep,
fighting off memories
when I'm awake.
I wouldn't wish this on anyone.

They ask if I'm doing okay,
if it hurts.
It does.
Just not the way they think.
I haven't let go of
what happened to us.

I watched the only man I ever loved,
fall out of love a little more
every single day.
I'm not scared to move on
from you.

I just can't let another in yet.

The reason this hurts is
because you don't date casually.
The reason you're with her is because
you believe you will love her.

I'm jealous that you
found a way to put your pieces
back together to give
to someone else.

I'm bitter that while I am afraid
of commitments, love, marriages,
you're already back on that track again.

I don't want you to be miserable,
I just want to know your secret.
I just want to love again, too.

10

Ghost

You haunted me for much longer than I expected you to.

It wasn't in the "I miss you" way. It was in the way that happens when another person becomes so entangled in your life that even when you separate and walk away, they still manage to appear.

When I was getting my first tattoo, I remembered how much you hated them.

When I first began writing so openly about things online, I remembered how much you liked to keep things private.

When a MuteMath song played on Spotify, I remembered you were the one who introduced me to them with a compilation CD.

When I fell in love again, you showed up in ghosts that told me no one would love me the way I was because you couldn't.

You were everywhere for such a long time, and I really didn't know how to remove you from this life I was trying to create for myself. This life that you weren't part of anymore. I wanted to remove everything about us. So I deleted all traces from social media. I cleansed my apartment of everything associated with you: love notes, cards, gifts, stuffed animals, and photographs. Yet I couldn't do that with memories. I couldn't rip them from my mind and toss them aside too, despite how desperately I wanted to.

Yet in the end, I knew I had to accept this. I had to accept that, like it or not, you were part of my life. A big part. An important part. An unforgettable part. So despite that, I healed, moved forward, and am living a life I'm proud of, your memory will always be around. And if I'm honest, I'm glad I have the ability to still remember that I once loved someone to such a degree that I would recall these things later on in my life. Because how sad would it be, really, to forget that you once loved someone so strongly that they made an imprint on you forever? How strong must a person be if they can still recall these kinds of things but they don't break them anymore?

So when those things do show up, when they do resurface, I'm not desperate to rip them apart. It's just a reminder that at some point, someone meant so much to me that I found it incredibly important to make sure they would be immortalized in my mind. And I think that says more about how much I'm capable of loving another person than it does about you, honestly.

I may not forget you, but remembering you won't break me, either.

11

I Wish I Had Written You Letters

I wish that when my mouth failed me
and I stood in silence,
I had thought to turn to pen and paper
since I couldn't turn to you.

If I had, then you would've read
all of my words
not just picked and chose
what you wanted to hear.

If I had, then you couldn't interrupt me
because ink on paper
is immovable and demands
to be noticed.

If I had, then it wouldn't have come out
in rambles and repetition,
in trains of thoughts that never finished,
looking for the right direction.

If I had, then it wouldn't
have said much.
only five words really,
that I couldn't seem to say out loud.

"Love me for me. Please."

If I had written you letters,
then maybe, just maybe
you might've finally heard me.

12

Blame

It wasn't *all* your fault.

At times, it felt easier to blame you. It felt easier to view you as someone who broke me down to an impossible degree, as someone who hurt me beyond belief, and to pretend that I had nothing to do with that. Because you *did* break me, and you *did* hurt me. I watched you fall out of love with me a little more every day, and it was something I didn't know how to handle. Yet when it came down to it, I knew I wasn't all innocent.

I allowed myself to become so wrapped up in you that I didn't know how to be a person outside of you. I had allowed my identity become "your girl" and "your fiancé" and I was content with that. I didn't really have goals or dreams outside of you and me. Back then, it didn't seem like a bad thing. It seemed to make all the sense in the world. Yet as we started having to face the real world, it was becoming apparent that you were more prepared for married life than I was. It was clear that I didn't feel confident to do anything on my own without you, and looking back I can see how frustrated you were. I can understand it because now that I do have a life with goals and dreams outside of us, I realize that before I was just being a shell of who I was. Maybe it was because I thought that was my role; maybe it was because I didn't have enough confidence to think I had anything to offer. But regardless of the reason, I wasn't anywhere near the person I could've been.

So maybe that's why you fell out of love with me. Maybe because you only saw a shell of a person.

When it all came crashing down I didn't understand and I couldn't process it, I stayed pretty wrecked for far too long. It was only when I became my own person that I understood that I hadn't been for so long. That I had lived in your shadow.

I'm sorry that back then, I tried to live in your shadow. I'm sorry that back then, I didn't step up and become my own whole person. Because maybe if I had, we either would've worked something out or we could've realized we weren't a good fit for each other long before those last few months that took a toll on us. Maybe we might've avoided some of that fallout.

Yet what's done is done. I just need you to know that I saw it wasn't all of your fault. I can take responsibility for my own mistakes too.

And I do.

13

Impossible

Thank you for making me believe in impossible things.

It may seem silly that the girl who is full of daydreams and optimism would have trouble believing in the things that seemed out of reach.

If it was up to me though, I would've always believed things were limited to imaginations, fantasies, and fiction novels.

You taught me that not everything that was unrealistic was necessarily impossible.

I mean, look at us. We were eight years apart in age, more different than the same, had a whole set of reasons set against us trying to tear us apart. And somehow we managed to make it three whole years. When it ended, it wasn't because of outside forces: not rumors, or parents, not exes, or pressure from everything around us. But because of *us*. We were the ones who chose to let go. It gave me courage in the future that, if someone I love and I wanted to hold on, then we would.

You were my impossible thing. The thing that shouldn't have worked for as long as it did, the thing that felt too much like a fairytale to be reality, the person I loved more than it seemed possible to love another person.

Because of you, I believe almost anything is possible now.

THIS WAS MY ALMOST LOVE

<u>14</u>

Downtown on July Fourth

I remember the day I decided
I wanted to know you better,
the day I looked at you and thought,
"There's something about him."

Sitting outside on a sidewalk,
watching this band led by a girl
with a golden voice,
and everyone is focused
on her playing and singing,
as well they should be,
because she's beautiful
and she's talented.

Yet I can't seem to look anywhere else but you.

Because the way you're playing that guitar,
the way you seemed to
thoroughly enjoy yourself
is something I've rarely seen in that way,
the way that says this is like
breathing for you.
Something so fascinating deserves attention, you know.

Because I've always been drawn
to people who have passions
and dreams and desires
that are written on their faces
Just as much as they are
tumbling from their mouths.

You're saying more than
you ever could
if you were speaking,
and all I want to do is find out,
what else makes your face light up this way.

Every person has their stories,
and it's on this day I decide
I want to know all of yours
That I want to be part of yours,

that I want you to be part of mine.

15

Confident

I gained my confidence back when I was with you.

Let me clarify that: I didn't gain my confidence back *because* of you. You just contributed. You still helped me and gave me the space to be myself, and that was the best thing anyone could've done for me.

Did I want to impress you? Of course I did. I liked you and I absolutely wanted you to like me. Yet I had made the decision that I was going to be myself—in every way. I wasn't going to hide behind filters or put on acts and hope you would buy it. If you were going to like me, you were going to like the honest, raw, actual me.

And boy, you did. You liked *me*.

Because I laughed way too much on our first date, and you told me you actually loved that I laughed so often.

Because you asked me about the one I loved first, you heard everything I had to say about him, and you still kissed me by the end of the night.

Because you knew I was a lot of optimism and excitement and instead of trying to talk me into being realistic, you just laughed and let me be.

We may not have spent as much time together as I would've wanted. Yet the times we were together were memories I held onto long after you were gone. Because you had me, boy. You had me in the most real form, and you didn't even know it. You didn't realize that this girl laying beside you was opening herself up to you, and that by doing that, she was loving herself. She was saying "This is who I am. I'm proud of her. I like her. I hope you do, too."

I wasn't living off of your compliments, because honestly you weren't one to give many. I wasn't sitting on the edge of my seat waiting to see what you thought of me. I was just being me, living life, and you just happened to be here too. Did I want us to work? More than you could know. More than I would've admitted to anyone else. Yet even when you walked away, you told me that no, it wasn't because of me, and maybe you were just trying to let me down easy. Yet I still choose to believe that it wasn't me, that despite how much I liked you, you just didn't like me enough to try harder than you did.

I didn't walk away feeling broken. I didn't walk away with my self-esteem at rock bottom. I walked away still loving me, still thinking highly of myself. Because I had allowed myself to be real and honest with someone and I gave my best shot trying to make something work out.

I knew I'd tried my hardest, and despite that we didn't last, I didn't feel like I'd failed. I never once looked at us as a mistake.

16

2 AM

It's a late night,
but you and your friends invite me out.
I probably should go home and sleep.
But I don't.

Hanging out doesn't mean Netflix and chill,
but truck rides at midnight.
I want to question if this is a safe thing.
But I don't.

They start driving, whipping around turns
and speeding on unfamiliar dirt roads.
"Boys will be boys," I justify,
"Maybe I should have just gone home."

But then you're laughing, eyes sparkling,
putting your arm around me,
and I'm leaning in,
hoping you won't let go.

You don't.

Not even when the truck jerks,
the tire flies off the axel,
leaving us stranded on an empty pathway,
making me nervous.

Everyone stays calm even though
panic is a natural first response,
and we're waiting for a tow truck
to hopefully get us home.
You still manage to put an arm around me,
and I'm hoping you won't let go.

You don't.

My imagination wants to run away with this.
It tries to paint a picture of this as the beginning,
and I know myself way too well.
If I let it, I'll read too much into this night.
So, I don't. Except that I do.

17

Honesty

Your honesty is still the thing that stands out the most to me. In a world of miscommunications, vague intentions, and games, you were clear.

You weren't perfect. You would leave hours between text messages and leave me with days or weeks between seeing you when we lived right across the street from each other. Yet when we broke up, you were honest. You tried to be kind; you told me it wasn't me, it was you, and maybe it was. Honestly, you had a lot going on. We both knew that I liked you more, that I was invested more, and when I was the one to say it out loud, you didn't deny it. It might have felt a little harsh, like a slap in the face, but the pain didn't last long. This was you, and the signs were rolling in from miles away long before I was sitting cross legged on your bed, trying to sort things out with you. You were honest, and you knew how to do what needed to be done when I wouldn't do it myself.

Later on, when you would tell me you had feelings for me again, you also told me that dating wasn't on the table, because you couldn't do a long distance relationship. I think people usually get angry about these things. Maybe if you were someone else, I might be. Yet, it was that blunt honesty, that straight-forward and to-the-point direction that I craved in the first place. When you complimented me, I knew you meant it. When you told me that you had feelings for me, I knew you meant that too. I also knew you weren't the kind of person to do things you really didn't want to do. I admired that, because I didn't know how to say "no" and how to stop things in progress, because I was always looking ahead at what might be, what could be. My hope extended to every place in my life, including you. Including us.

Yet you, you were always honest with yourself and with everyone around you. It's why I think we stayed friends, even now. I knew that when we continued to stay in contact, even after the romantic aspect of us was gone, that you still wanted me in your life somehow. I will never thank you enough for being honest. I never took that for granted, even if I never actually told you.

I wish I had told you.

<u>18</u>

"Why did things not work out between us?"

"I couldn't reciprocate the level of affection you had for me and you deserved better."

I have played out
One thousand ways
One thousand possibilities
One thousand reasons
One thousand lives
That take me left instead of right,
You instead of me,
Us instead of forks in the roads
that sent us in opposite paths.

Yet it's clear to me that in every
way, chance, life,

We would find a reason to let go.

19

Passive

There was one night, one that I can't forget even if I tried. It was me, and it was you. It was the last night before you were heading back home for summer break. The last night where coming to see you only meant crossing the street from my apartment to your dorm room. Tomorrow, you'd be back home, an hour away, and I think we both knew that once that happened, you would probably not make any special trips just to see me.

So here I am, sitting on your bed, and I'm all at once trying to remember this moment, remember me and you and laughing and kissing and all of these things that I'm hoping won't fade from my memory once you drive away. Here I am, trying to remember you and wondering if you will remember me too—because whatever this thing is that we've kept going, it doesn't have a label, and things not labeled tend to be tossed in boxes and shoved in closets, forgotten and misplaced.

And in the midst of all of this I remember you're telling me "I like you. And not just because we make out sometimes. I genuinely care about you as a person." And despite my optimistic nature, despite how much I like you, all I can think of is "Do you? Why is that not enough to try?" But I don't say it. I never say it. So you walk me to my car, and this is supposed to be the end, this is supposed to be the moment where we say goodbye and I go home wondering "Does he really care about me?"

As we approach my car, there is a shadow in the passenger seat that I'm not familiar with. The shadow turns out to be a person, a stranger sitting completely still. All I feel is panic and confusion and I can't think straight. While I'm just standing there, you are the one who stepped forward. You were the one who opened the door and saw that the figure was a drunk college student, someone you knew. It was you who would try to spend the next hour coaxing this guy to get out of my car, while having me sit inside yours. It was you who would approach me and give me your keys, telling me to drive your car home and that you would bring mine to me in the morning, that you wanted to make sure I was safe.

When I tell you that you don't have to do this, It's you who says "I don't want to be passive about this!" I hear this and it puts me at ease, knowing you've got this. It's me who's wishing that you were saying this about us, that you didn't want to be passive about you and me and what we could be. Yet despite that, it's in this moment that I knew that yes, you do care about me. That I do mean something to you, despite that you'll still drive away tomorrow morning.

I know that honestly, you would have done this for anyone else. It's the kind of person you are. Yet it was that night that let me put us to rest. That night, where you stepped up and made sure I'd be okay. Where you proved that you did care about me. I never questioned it again after that. Even now, I still don't.

Thank you.

<u>20</u>

I Wish

Nothing ever felt forced with you.
Nothing ever felt heavy or complicated or out of place.
It was simply you and me and that was enough, boy,
that was enough.

Everything was open with you.
You were someone that made me feel comfortable;
I knew I could talk about anything going on in my head
or we could sit content in the quiet
and that was enough.

I remember you as someone
that made things feel so easy without even trying
that made silence seem preferable to speaking in the best way
that made me wish we hadn't run out of months
that made me wish there weren't so many miles between.

I wish somehow, I'd been enough
for you.

21

My Brain is Still Full of You

I sometimes wonder how much more
knowledge I would hold
if my brain weren't filled with song lyrics
and the words you spoke to me
when you thought we were a possibility

Maybe I would master sign language
or understand those complex equations
in statistics.

Instead, I'm attempting to figure out the chances
that you and I would come back together again,
and the probability of whether that would be
a good thing.

I never seem to fully master
the things I grow passionate about
because my mind wanders too many
different places to pick just one.
I'm always investing half my mind
in places it can't hold onto.

I could be working on that book I talk about,
and learning how to become a better writer.

I could store in my head all the names
of the people I meet.

Instead I remember your favorite color
and the way you felt about Damien Rice's music.
I remember the ridiculous faces you made
just to get a smile out of someone.

Instead of the things that move you forward
my brain holds onto things
that make me want to stay.

22

Roadmap

You had one of the biggest impacts on my life.

I have a bad habit of over-romanticizing things; and I'll be the first to admit it. Yet we didn't feel romantic. You didn't feel like a soul mate, you just felt like a place to breathe, a place to just be. I think the thing that always killed me about our relationship is that you had no idea just how much you did for me in that short time. Just how much being with you and that time in my life gave me. I don't feel like I did that much for you. Not for lack of trying, and not because I was a bad girlfriend, but I think that what I could give wasn't something you wanted or were looking for. While you, on the other hand, changed my life in some ways. I know that sounds crazy and overwhelming and too much, but god, you did. And you did it without trying at all. It was just you. The person you were brought out the person I wanted to be and every moment I spent with you was a moment I felt more like I was breathing easy for the first time again. The person you were made me feel at home in myself even though I couldn't make a home in you, because we weren't home, we were an apartment on a lease, a countdown clock with never enough time. The person you were, just by being you, it was exactly what I needed at the time and it convinced me that every once in awhile, timing just gives you someone who can make you feel different and the way you want to be. You were that for me, and I wish over and over that I could have expressed that to you without making it sound like I was madly in love, because no, that's not it. There is no way I could ever express things to you without sounding like poetry, but that's how my tongue likes to twist itself when I talk about you. It talks about you in prose and in iambic pentameter, and people read it and think "Wow she is in love, wow she is in love." And I want to scream, "No, it was something different, it was something better."

You were something better. You were a roadmap that helped lead me back to the beginning of myself and all I can do is thank you one thousand times over for being that. By being you.

23

What If's are the Worst Questions but They Are All I Ever Ask

You will never be the one I run to when things get hard,
but I've thought about it.
You will never be the one I come home to,
but I've thought about it.
You will never be the one who sees the person I'll become,
but I've thought about it.
You will never be the one I say that I love wholeheartedly,
but I've thought about it.

I will never be the one you love wholeheartedly,
but I wonder if you've thought about it, too.

24

Almost

I always wondered if I would've loved you.

If I'm honest, I really think I could have. I didn't have the chance; our time was just too short. Some people claim love at first sight, but the only thing I can say for certain that I thought at first sight was "He seems interesting. I want to know him better."

And lucky me, I did get to know you better. I did learn that your face wasn't always serious and that you loved Kevin Hart, that you would lose your mind watching a UK basketball game or listening to Snarky Puppy live and that you could quote every line of *Cool Runnings*. I learned that you had a unique singing voice and that you played guitar better than almost anyone I knew. I learned that you were honest and straight forward, but that you are probably the worst texter I've ever come across in my life, that you were just as comfortable in silence as you were in conversation.

You were you, and I liked everything about you, even the parts that drove me crazy.

Every moment I spent with you I remember as good. I don't remember walking away without thinking of them as anything less. I did walk away wondering if this was the start of something more. Because with you, more didn't seem like something scary or intimidating. It felt like we were always one step away from more. We were like lighting matches with the friction of "Will we? Won't we?" We always felt like anticipation, like that thing on the tip of my tongue or the words caught in my throat that refused to surface. Like a roller coaster approaching that hill, the one that would launch us to the next place. Yet we stopped just shy of it. We stayed suspended, abandoned right before we could reach the top, before we could even look and see what might've been before us. God only knows if the reason we didn't work out is because we pulled the emergency break out of fear or if it's because we were just never meant to make that leap; if our car would've derailed off the tracks, if we wouldn't have survived it after all.

Never knowing is the only option that is left, and I still wonder if I would've loved you had I been given the chance. Yet those weren't the cards we were dealt. This wasn't the path we chose, and so I will settle for the fact that in the time I did have you, I think you knew beyond a shadow of a doubt that I cared about you. That you know even now, with our friendship, I still do.

I hope you know.

THIS IS
THE ONE
I COULD HAVE
LOVED

25

The Way I Remember You

I have this memory of one Fourth of July
waiting for fireworks to start,
waiting for explosions of color
to add beauty to the dark sky.

They light the match, I hear the sound
and the firework shoots up,
but instead of shooting towards the sky,
it explodes only a few feet over my head.

The sound is deafening and sparks are flying
all around me, and my heart is beating
against my chest so hard
that it threatens to rip right through.

My skin feels like those sparks
landed all over them,
and I should be terrified,
because this is dangerous
and not the way it's supposed to happen.
Yet all I do
is laugh,

and laugh,
and laugh.

That's the way I remember you.

I think you should've intimidated me.
Green eyes and twice my height,
The kind of smile that eases nerves,
Yet sets them on edge at the same time.

You weren't supposed to be anywhere near me.
I was just as content watching you from miles away,
watching you light up the room with
your charm and your wit.

Yet instead there you were,
exploding only a couple feet above my head,
and all I can see are sparks everywhere.
Bright, beautiful, radiant sparks.

Every time you pulled me in
my heart thudded so loudly
against my chest,
I wanted to apologize for the noise.

You grabbed my face to kiss me,
and I felt I would fall apart any second,
or explode right there on the ground.

This feeling was something
so bold and bright and overwhelming,

and it should have been terrifying,
but instead I'm just laughing and smiling,

and I don't fully understand if I know
just how dangerous this is—
this feeling that threatens to rip me apart even though
I don't know anything about you.

You're just like that memory of the Fourth of July.
You started to fade as quickly as you showed up,
but I still managed to keep you alive
on my pages and in my stories.

<u>26</u>

Hurricane

There are two types of people when it comes to hurricanes.

There are the people who hear the warnings in advance and immediately seek shelter. They prepare themselves and the ones they love, they go to their basements and safe spaces, and they wait for the storm to pass. They board up windows and never even think about doing what it takes to stay as far away as possible.

Then, there are the people who hear the sirens. They listen to the weather reports and they too prepare their loved ones and get them to a safe place. As for themselves? You'll find them watching out their windows, or even standing outside on their porches and yards. They watch as the storm takes shape, as it begins to shift, as it begins to make its direction right towards them.

And they don't move.

Maybe they have a death wish, maybe they are simply in awe at the power of something larger than themselves. They know they need to walk back inside, shut the door, and never look back. They hear the sirens and the warnings. They don't believe themselves invincible. Yet they continue to watch with wide eyes and nervous hands and blood pumping through their veins; waiting.

I was that kind of person, and you were a hurricane if I ever saw one.

I stood outside and watched you coming right towards me, and I didn't even try to run. I didn't even try to guard myself despite the sirens, despite the warnings, despite the people telling me to take shelter. Maybe I thought you could find shelter in a storm, maybe I just wanted to know what it was like to be swept away in a feeling that feels bigger than you. You may have been a hurricane, but I wouldn't call you destructive- you didn't rip me apart. You just scattered me, left me feeling confused.

Maybe I just wanted to be reckless and maybe I thought once you were gone so would my memories of you too. Because you can't hold onto something that never stayed, right? Yet somehow you took root in me, and I never expected that while you would never stay in one place, you had made a permanent home in my bones.

I would've been just as content being your friend, I would've been just as content with getting to know you in that way, because I always found you to be interesting and someone I wanted to know better.

I would've been just as content standing on my front porch watching you from miles and miles away, never coming close.

But you swept me up in you for only a few moments and it took my breath and it took my sanity and clarity, scattering it every which way. It took the parts of me that I thought were calm and thought were hidden and uncovered them. It took intensity and adrenaline I didn't even know I possessed and exposed it. You were here and you were gone and I was left standing in the middle of rubble, but I didn't even mind. I almost wanted to be a storm chaser in that moment, but instead I just tried to forget I'd ever seen the storm in the first place.

That I'd ever seen a storm quite like you.

27

Something

When it's all said and done, it's probably strange that I'm writing about you, isn't it? We were never anything official. Honestly, I don't think I could say for certain that we were anything. Yet somehow you, of all people, made me feel something intense that I couldn't shake, even after you were gone.

Let me clear this up right now—I wasn't in love with you.

However, the way I did feel...there really is no way to explain. I don't know how to encompass or make sense of the way I felt around you. You didn't have to try, you didn't have to do anything, and yet it was simply something about you that caused my heart to beat so hard it hurt, to make me feel like I was always on edge, to make me feel an adrenaline rush like I had just dived off of a cliff. And all you had to do was walk in a room, look at me, and smile.

I know. it doesn't make sense to me either.

So you can only imagine what it was like when you would hold my hand jokingly. Or hug me for a little longer than necessary. Or crack a joke while making a straight face about wanting to make out. Somehow I managed to keep it together, somehow I managed to act like these things weren't driving me crazy in the best way. Sometimes I wondered if it was written all over my face, or if you could hear my heartbeat. Yet if you noticed, you never said a word.

And so I would go home and think about you and I would wonder if I was on your mind when you didn't see me. I would wonder how many other girls were lying in their beds thinking about you too, because I knew I wasn't the only one. I wondered how I could possibly spend this much time thinking about someone who I knew for a fact I would never have a real relationship with. I wondered how someone can find a way into your thoughts without trying, how they can become someone you think about often while you are uncertain if they think of you at all.

I would wonder how someone I didn't love could take up so much room in me.

28

Maybe I'm the Punchline

I think in the grand scheme of things,
We were kind of a joke.
One of those endless anecdotes
that holds a lot of details,
until the punchline hits
and you remember it's supposed to be funny.

It was supposed to be funny,
When after your girlfriend broke your heart,
You joked that you'd have to put attention elsewhere,
While looking straight at me.
So we laughed about it.

It was supposed to be funny,
Every time you asked if I wanted to make out,
while our friends were sitting on the couch
knowing of course we would do no such thing.
So we all laughed about it.

It was supposed to be funny,
While we drove around in my car
on a winter night
you told me to look straight ahead,

So you could kiss me on the cheek.
My face turned blood red,
and we both laughed about it.

So many little jokes,
Packed into such a short amount of time.
So perhaps when you stopped talking to me for awhile,
I figured this was just another joke.
I kept laughing. Kept waiting.

Perhaps when our friends mention,
That you're moving out of the state,
I assume it's another joke.
I assume that it's not true, until I hear it from you.
Yet still all I can do is laugh about it.

Maybe if I keep laughing,
keep pretending we were just a joke,
It won't hurt so much when
you're not here anymore.

Perhaps maybe I thought
We weren't joking all along.
It's supposed to be funny,
so maybe I'm the punchline.

29

Women

My friends were never really that fond of you, you know.

Not our mutual friends—no, they all liked you. We spent a lot of time together, laughing and joking around, listening to music, just having conversations. We all thoroughly enjoyed each other's company. Our mutual friends were also all guys.

It was the women in my life who weren't fans of you.

I am friends with strong women, intelligent women, the kind that keep me steady when my head is in the clouds and my heart is running wild. They are the kind of women who know their worth, know what they want, and go after it. They are the kind of women you look at and think "They are a force to be reckoned with." They are the ones who have to remind me about reality. They were the ones saying "Watch out."

Whether you had hurt them, or their sister, or they just didn't get a good vibe from you, not a single girl said "You should go for it! He's wonderful!" and that probably should've been a red flag right there. If all of these women, who held qualities I wanted to have and who are more grounded in the real world than I ever could be, all seemed to agree that you weren't the best guy, that should've been enough to turn around and not have anything else to do with you, right? Yet I could never seem to agree with them.

I could agree in theory with them. I could say "You're right, this isn't going to work out." And I believed it, because it was true. Yet when I would see you, none of those things seemed to matter. Because when I was around you, you didn't seem like that kind of person. I never saw the sides of you that broke other people, I never witnessed any part of you that their words portrayed. They were angry at you, but I never could be. Maybe because I knew that I could've avoided you from the start, I could've stopped anything before it started, but I didn't. So if I had to be angry I would have to be angry at myself.

You were always you. You were always going to leave. I just thought I was strong enough to handle you for awhile and then walk away without you having a real effect on me.

I was wrong.

30

One More Night Before You Go

"Your bark is worse than your bite."
"You only think that, until I bite you."

Tonight I'll forget that this is a bad idea,
That everything about this- about us- is temporary.

Just give me a memory to hold onto,
And God knows I'll grasp onto it for dear life.

You show up in my door frame,
Walking in and not saying much at all.

You pull me in and finally kiss me
for the first time, for the last time.

You'll always be a cliffhanger,
Giving me just enough rope that I struggle to grasp onto.

Honestly, perhaps I should let you go,
But what is worse?

Bloodied, calloused, blistered hands,
Or reality?

31

Wanted

I stayed hung up on you longer than I'd ever want to admit to myself or to anyone else.

In the short time we knew each other, you said some things that stuck in my brain, even long after you left. I remember once you told me, "No one really knows who I am. Not even you." and that kind of a statement is maddening to me, because I want to know people. I wanted to know you.

You never really gave me that chance. Maybe that was your point, maybe not. Regardless, you were someone I really wanted to know, wanted to discover, just simply wanted in general. You were someone I never would have.

I asked myself at least 1,723,435 times why you. How does someone who shows up in your life for such a short time leave that kind of impact on you, the kind that follows you around for weeks and months? It didn't make sense to miss you. It didn't make sense to think about you.

Yet you were the one to open a lot of doors and then never close them.

To be fair, I will take blame in this. I look at things from every possible angle and let them play out in my head. I should've been the one to cut everything off and close all those doors that you could walk back through.

Yet, I never knew what to expect from you on any given day, and that left an endless amount of possibilities to think about. So I did. I let my mind play out all of those possibilities and paths that might've been taken.

And then you left, and it should've been the end of it, really. It should've been the door closed, a chapter finished. Yet instead you left all the ends loose and all the doors cracked open, enough to pop your head in every once in a while to remind me you were still here.

A reminder that no, I will never get close, and no, I will never have more than just a few moments talking to you, but that nonetheless you would keep showing up, keep reappearing.

It was infuriating and it was the worst, and I never stopped it, because as much as I wanted you to close the door, I never could seem to do it myself. I could never make myself imagine a possibility where I cut you out and never gave you an opening to come back.

I think I always hoped someday our paths might cross again, that you would come in the door and close it behind you, and maybe we could finish what we almost started. Maybe I was hoping that one day you would actually stick around for awhile to see what could've been.

Maybe I always hoped that you would just stay.

32

Even My Mother Sees Your Name Written All Over My Face

My mother sees my cheeks blush
as I say the name of
the new city you live in.
How my voice becomes quiet
at the sound of your name.

"You still like him.
You don't want to,
You fight it, but
You do."

So I guess I should be grateful
for your nomad spirit,
because if you stayed in one place,
stayed in this place,
I would never find a way
to get over you.

33

I Wish You Hadn't Kissed Me That Night

I wish you hadn't kissed me that night.

I won't say I didn't want you to, because I did.
I won't say it was a bad memory, because it wasn't.

I'm saying that maybe if you hadn't kissed me on that night,
Maybe if you'd kissed me on some other night,
Like you joked about doing 1,000 times,
It would've been easier to handle when you were gone.

Yet instead, you kissed me after I found out you were leaving,
After I found out this fact from everyone else but you,
After I had to accept that this thing between us,
that wasn't actually a thing,
Was over and done.

And you chose then to kiss me.
A kiss that felt urgent, because it was never happening again,
A kiss that said "This is what could've been but won't be."
A kiss that confirmed that yes, there was a connection,
Or at least enough attraction that you were on my couch that night
Instead of someone else's.

You chose to kiss me that night, and I never could get it out of my mind.

34

Possibilities

I think the reason I felt so strongly about you is because you were a limitless amount of possibilities.

You were unreadable. It was impossible for me to tell what you were thinking or how you were feeling. You would share parts of yourself that you wanted to share, but also be intentional on letting people know there was so much more to you that you wouldn't talk about. That kind of thing makes a person like me crazy.

I live in a world of possibilities. I live in a world where every path is open and anything is possible until I'm shown that it is not possible after all. My mind will run down paths, no matter how unlikely, because everything is plausible. It works no differently when it comes to people.

Especially when it comes to people.

Because until I get to know a person better, until they've shared parts of themselves with me, then for all I know all options are still on the table. So when someone like you comes along, always leaving more questions than answers behind them, it's insanity. It's things that keep me up at night and things that haunt me during the day.

I was close enough to think about you but never felt close enough to ask you why you were this way.

In all the time I've known people, I've never had a person come into my life, make memories with me, make me feel certain ways, and manage to leave without my knowing who they were in the end. You were the one who managed to do just that, and so my mind does what it always does; it ran through the possibilities of you that were still open. You left so many open.

So my mind ran itself ragged, chasing this path and that one, retracing steps and taking new routes, hoping to piece together something that felt like clarity or closure. Something that could let me say "Oh, this is why. This is how it would've happened." Because I've always had that. I've always found a way to understand.

You, on the other hand, were far beyond my understanding. The sooner I understood that, the sooner I was able to set aside all these questions, all these ideas and possibilities, and try to move forward. You still would pop back in every so often, and my mind would want to jump at the chance of chasing you and your reasons again. Yet after so long, I finally became tired.

I finally became tired of chasing a possibility and an answer from you.

35

FTHR MTN

One of your band's T-shirts sits folded in my bottom drawer.

I packed it with me to college,
because it showed a picture of Kentucky.
I wanted to take a little bit of home with me,
I wasn't asking to take a little bit of you with me too.

I wore it out one day,
and people had compliments
to toss in my direction,
and honestly I forgot why
I stopped wearing it in
the first place.

Then someone asked me,
"Where did you get it?"
"What are those letters on the back?"
"What are those words inside?"

My closed mouth filled itself with descriptions
Of green eyes and quick smiles
and shows in
Coffeehouses
and
Car garages

and
You.

Instead I said,
"It's just a local band from back home."

As if I didn't know you,
As if I didn't want to.

I took off the T-shirt.
I placed it back in the bottom drawer.
I haven't worn it since.

36

Future

I never could see a future with you. Isn't that strange?

Isn't it strange that I could think about someone so often and feel something so strong rattling inside my ribcage, but not envision a future with you in it? I won't say I didn't try. I won't say I never pondered, *What if we did?* but at the same time I knew that it wouldn't happen.

I couldn't see you as the kind of guy to call me baby and hold my hand on crowded sidewalks. I couldn't picture introducing you to my parents and letting my family get to know you. I couldn't piece together any mental image of you looking at me and telling me "I love you." I couldn't picture myself running into your arms after a bad day or falling asleep beside you at night. It wasn't because I didn't think you were capable of those things, because I know you had relationships and you did all of that before. I just couldn't match you up to being that for *me*.

Maybe it's because things happened so fast, maybe it's because we never had a chance, but when I thought about you I couldn't picture a future. My head would just flood with memories of green eyes and charm and laughter. It was just mental videos rewinding and replaying, wondering if maybe I missed something, wondering if I imagined everything all along.

It would also replay the last night we were in my apartment, the night you said you were sorry that you were moving and that things couldn't work out. I would replay it and this time ask you, "How did you feel about this?" and "Would we really have become anything more?" I would've been brave and asked for answers to questions that would rack my brain later on. At the time I was just trying to live in the moment, because I didn't know if I'd ever see you again, and trying to pretend like I didn't care about you as much as I did. I wish I had thought to ask; I wish I'd thought to not let you walk away without giving me something to put whatever we had to rest.

I couldn't change the past and I couldn't see a future with you, so it simply left me in the present. It simply left me in a place where I didn't know how to cope besides to just let this feeling, this way I felt about you, overwhelm me and pass through. Hoping that eventually my heart wouldn't react when it heard your name or I wouldn't do a double take when I saw someone who looked like you. Hoping that eventually when you would tell me you were coming back to town it wouldn't take me back to the memories, it wouldn't get my hopes up on whether I would see you or not.

Eventually, you wouldn't affect me the way you used to. That's the only future for us that I was certain I could hold onto.

37

You're Still a Good Memory

Not every moment with you
was confusing or complicated.

In fact, the actual memories
I have of you,
are all good,
all worth remembering.

It was all the space in between
that made everything cloudy;
you had a way of clearing
all the smoke screens
once you walked in.

The actual memories I have of you
are still worth remembering,
and from time to time,
I still do.

38

Friends

Feelings are a complicated sort, aren't they?

They can be exhilarating and they can be exciting, they can be strong indicators of a connection you have with someone, or simply a way for you to see what is attractive to you.

And then sometimes they just get in the way. They don't let you see the things you really want; the things you really need.

I think at the end of the day, I just wanted to know you. Because I love getting to know interesting and complex people. I love hearing their stories and seeing their vulnerability and seeing the things that made them who they are. More often than not, people do open up around me. Yet not you.

That was enough to keep you on my mind. That was enough to make me wonder "why?" and I didn't fully understand the reasons you would resurface in my head. My friends would ask why
I was still hung up on you, and didn't I know you wouldn't be good for me, and didn't I know we would've never ended up together? And I did. I knew all of those things. Yet it didn't seem to be about that. It didn't feel like I needed to know why we didn't try something more- I knew those answers. So what was it? If my romantic feelings about you had their closure, why were you still here?

Because I believe I honestly just wanted to be your friend, and I couldn't even get that far, it seems.

I think right now we might call ourselves friends. Yet it feels like acquaintances. It's the "I know that guy" response if you're ever brought up. Yet if I saw you in public, face to face, I feel like we wouldn't really have much to say besides small talk. I hate small talk, and I don't think you're a fan of it either. I'd like to be able to sit down and have a real conversation with you. I'd like to see you and not wonder if approaching you would result in an awkward exchange of "How are you?" "Good, you?" I don't want that. When I call someone a friend, I know that even after six months of not speaking to them, I can still reach out to tell them something important and it will matter to them. It will be something they will celebrate in with me, and I would do the same for them. We don't have that, and the only reason I can see why is because you don't want that.

In the end, I saw potential in a friendship that never really came about. Maybe because I let infatuation beat me to it, maybe it's because regardless you would've never opened that door in the first place. Yet I've never had someone come into my life, affect me, and then just leave. You did, and I may never know for certain if you and I will ever have that connection.

Despite how many doors that were left open, that is one that I know I can close.

39

You Don't Live in My Heart Anymore, but You Still Found Places to Make Yourself at Home

You don't live in my heart anymore.
Time is a funny thing, it brings new things,
And it evicts others from the places they've made home.
You never asked to live here,
You never knew you lived here.
Yet I paid the rent with memories and what if's,
Buying you a little more time.

I learned almost immediately
That the feelings overwhelming me,
Would not go away in a day, or a week,
Or a month. It would take time
The more I fought, the longer it wanted to stay.

So I gave in and I let it happen,
I gave in and let you affect me,
Let you consume me for awhile,
Even after you were gone.

I know you can never fully rid yourself

Of people and pasts and ghosts and hopes.
They find their way into different spaces,
Empty spaces, places to hide away when
Your heart opens its door to someone new.

My heart doesn't skip a beat when
They say your name anymore,
Oh, but my bones still ache
Always restless,
Always whispering,
"Oh, I remember."

40

I Don't Think About You as Much Anymore

There will come a day
Where I won't care
Where you've moved to,
Won't wonder
How you're doing or
If I'll ever see you again.

A day I won't think about
You all that much.

I know, because
It's already begun.

41

Nothing

I don't know how I'm supposed to remember you. When memories of you sift through my mind, bringing back to life your smile or your laugh, they don't know what feelings to bring back with them. It's simpler when we can have a label, some category to put our experiences in. It makes it a bit easier to swallow when it's all said and done. Yet sometimes we don't have the mercy of a label. There isn't always a clean understanding where you gain clarity.

You held no label, and I have no basis to this day on what to make of you.

I wish I knew where you fit in. On days where you came to visit me at work and the days where we talked about things that had happened in your life, I felt like we were friends. The nights where you kissed my cheek or my forehead and told me I looked beautiful, you seemed like a boyfriend. When I heard you were moving away, from everyone else *but* you, it felt like I was nothing at all.

The night you came to my apartment and really kissed me, I felt like you were an almost. Someone who might've been, but would never be. I think if I'm honest I could admit that here or there, we would have never been. We would have traveled in the same circles, of changing labels every encounter until it wore one or both of us down.

The mention of your name still wears me down.

We like to believe that we are better than this. We like to believe that we won't get caught up in people who take us in circles. We believe we can get on the ride for as long as we want. We don't feel, we don't assume, and then we get off when we get sick of it. I've never known how to do that, though. I certainly didn't want to do that with you. I stayed on the ride trying to figure it out. You would leave, return, ask to see me, and I'd come back every time.

We promise ourselves we are better than this. We tell ourselves we are worth more, that we deserve more. When I was out of your gravity, I knew this wasn't the way things were supposed to be. Yet, the first utterance of, "Wow, you look beautiful today" made my entire resolve break down completely.

The last time you asked to see me, I said yes. Yet when you bailed at the last second, that was the night that finally woke me up from whatever this game was that we were playing. You were not, nor would you ever be, someone I would end up with. We had no type of relationship. You weren't my friend. You weren't more. You were just you. And everything you were seemed to shake up everything I was.

So for my sake, and my sanity, I decided that I couldn't keep trying to figure out where you fit into my life. So I stopped trying.

I wonder about you from time to time. I hope you're doing well, and I hope your life is going exactly the way you want it to. And I can only hope that there aren't dozens of other girls who can't determine what label you are in their lives. I'd like to hope you're better than that. I wouldn't hope for anything else.

THIS WAS
LOVING MY
BEST &
FRIEND

<u>42</u>

Was It Worth It?

There will never be a good way to explain
what happens when two people who
have been around each other constantly
for years upon years without feeling anything
more than platonic
suddenly start to think maybe there is
more.

That maybe this is something
worth fighting for,
that if everything we already have
that is priceless could suddenly
become more.

It can become more, we learned that, darling,
But it can cost you more, too.

43

Change

You were the game-changer.

You took the broken shards of a shattered heart and didn't pretend you knew how to put them together again, but you did step carefully trying not to break them more. You took all of the games and confusion, the "I'll call you today and walk away tomorrow" moments, the not wanting labels and not wanting exclusivity, and you tossed them out the window.

The only thing you wanted to take from me was my hand.

This all felt too foreign to me. This didn't feel normal. I had become used to hours and days between text messages, used to riddles instead of poetry, used to kissing without commitments and feeling without reciprocation. I'm used to being the one giving and giving without much in return. So here you are, with your quick replies and your straight-forward feelings towards me. Here you are with your intentions on the table and your eyes on me filled with excitement about us.

You were something different, and I didn't know what to do with that. I wanted to accept it, I wanted to go all in like I had once done in what felt like another life. Yet it was impossible for me to do that anymore. I was still healing my broken heart from before, and I didn't know if it was stable enough to let anyone else in just yet.

I didn't know how to express that to you; because all I knew was how things felt. Because as much as I knew you were what I needed, as much as my mind knew this was a good thing, the only feeling I was consumed with was fear. Fear that I'd hurt you, that you would hurt me, that you would be another name on a list of broken hopes. You had been in my life for six years, I didn't want you to be a faded memory.

In all of the times I was afraid, all the times I ran away and told you, "Not now, I'm not ready," you still managed to keep those things about you. You stayed the same and when it was all said and done, I knew that walking away from you would be something I would regret.

You were someone who didn't crumble when I took off, and you were still standing when I was finally ready to try.

When I was finally ready for you.

44

Scared Summer

I was scared all year,
that wasn't anything new.

You kept telling me I was beautiful,
knowing I could walk away any second.
You kept telling me I was worth the world,
and you tried to give me as much as you knew how.

Summer is meant for flings and scorching romances,
but you treated me like Spring,
watching for new life to come from something that died.
You were willing to wait. You knew change didn't happen in a
month.

You told me I was worth waiting for,
worth holding on to,
worth holding hands in public,
holding hearts in private.

I took one step forward,
and twelve steps back,
because I kept wanting to trust you,
but I couldn't even trust myself.

I was a scared summer,
but you were a consistent autumn,

just waiting for the leaves to fall.
Waiting for a new start.

Autumn is filled with
scattered leaves, changing colors,
lighting bonfires, starting flames.
Everything has no choice but to change.

I was ready for a change.

45

Falling For Your Best Friend

I don't think that people realize what it's like to fall in love with their best friend.

On the one hand it's exciting and comforting, even. This is a person who you have established a solid foundation with. A person you have already made memories with and who has made you laugh so hard you wanted to cry. A person who has tried in the best ways they knew how to be there for you even when they weren't certain how to do that. A person who knew your family and you knew theirs, and it wasn't hard to strike up conversations on either side. This person sees you when you're not trying to impress anybody, when you're having an off day, or when you are being your best self. A person like that, who turns into a romantic relationship, is hard to find and you are incredibly lucky if you both fall in love with each other.

Then, there is the other side. The side that comes out when you're dating. It's the exploration of someone you thought you knew everything about, only to discover there are still things you don't know. It's to find out what they are like when they get angry, or all of their childhood memories, or how they show love and affection. You may have seen a version of these things before, but it's different now. It's deeper now.

It's a point where you have to decide if you want to take this journey with someone you have always called your best friend, or if you want to try and salvage what you had before. Sometimes, it's not easy. Sometimes you wonder, "What if it doesn't work out? What if I lose them?"

It's scary, and I'll tell you, I almost didn't want to do it, because I would risk losing you.

Yet ultimately I can see this was worth it. I can see that knowing you on a deeper level—all the good, bad, and ugly layer—made me love you even more. It made me fall for you in a way I couldn't imagine, because I wasn't falling for a perfect person or a Prince Charming. I was falling for a person who was wonderful but also broken, creative but also temperamental, interesting but also my polar opposite in so many ways. It's the kind of love that didn't stand for being mistreated, but also didn't shut someone out at the first sign of trouble. It's a love that didn't stop when our similarities did, but cared enough to grow on it's own, and to grow together at that.

It built its own house together, and baby I honestly think we built something beautiful. I don't think it would've been nearly as wonderful if we hadn't built ourselves on a strong foundation first. A foundation built on our past together and our past apart. Both of our strengths nailing down floorboards to even the other out, so that while it may have had a few bumps across the way, the house didn't lean more to one side or another. It stood firm on something we didn't even know we were putting together.

It's something we should be proud of, even if we didn't end up living there after all.

46

I Hoped You Would Be the One to Stay

Shaky hands made steady,
restless feet stop running,
wandering eyes quit searching
for someone else.

Have I ever told you
that your eyes are the most
beautiful colors I've ever seen?

Have I ever told you
that you make me want to believe
love can win a second time?

Have I ever told you
that you're someone I hope
is still here tomorrow?
and the next day. And the next day.

And the next…

47

Hurt

You were the first person I ever thought I would hurt.

In all the years I've been in relationships or have been involved with someone, there has been a very common theme; I've always been the one who cared more. I've always been the one who loved harder, who loved the most, and the one still holding on when others let go. It's just been my role and I learned to accept it.

Then you came along, and for the first time, it appeared that someone actually might love me the same. Possibly even more than me, because while you were encouraging me that this was a good thing, and great thing, I was still holding onto reservations and fears. I wasn't sure if love was worth another shot right then, and for the first time in my life someone was to trying to coax me out from the shadows. I hadn't had someone saying, "I know you're scared, but this is worth it."

Yet I was still working through a few things: trying to figure out why others hadn't stayed, trying to keep my heart intact, worrying that I was never going to be quite good enough to love. I was letting my fears run me and I didn't know how to fix it. My only options were to shut you out and walk away or dive in and hope for the best. In either situation all I could envision was me hurting you, and hurting myself. It felt like either choice would result in the possibility of us getting hurt.

You knew all of this, because I told you. Somehow you were the only person I ever felt comfortable enough saying things like this out loud to. You would listen intently and nod your head, never taking your eyes off of me as I rattled off all my reasons and all my worries, thinking that you would finally see me as too much baggage, as too much in general. Yet you never did. You simply took my hand and said, "I know it's a long shot, but I still want this. I want you."

It's terrifying when you think you might be the one to cause the pain. I think as much as it hurts to be the one hurting, it's that much worse to know that you're the one who caused it. That it was in your hands and your choices caused them suffering. It's terrifying when you have no idea if you will hurt them, but you know there is a chance. The thought of it is enough to make you want to leave before you even begin.

I almost did, boy. I almost did.

48

Cold Feet

You ask me why my feet are always frozen.
I smile and think,
"Baby, if you only knew."

The phrase "cold feet" was something used to describe me.

My feet don't know the difference between
Running from things that hurt
And running from things that heal.

I have to keep repeating to myself
"Stay, this is a good thing."

"Stay. Aren't you tired of running?"

49

Timing

I've always been someone to blame time and timing for things not working out.

I have always liked to make time and timing my scapegoat. I've always been the one who tried to scramble pieces together and when they didn't fit, say that it was all because of timing. I would make excuses saying if I'd only met them five years later or five years before, if I hadn't been in a bad place, if they had been in a better one, then maybe we would've had a shot. Regardless of how many flaws might've been the culprit, I always believed that time and timing is what makes or breaks us.

You, darling, turned everything I knew on it's head. Because by all odds, we never had the right timing.

When you first told me you had feelings for me, it came as a shock. Partially because you were 18, and I was 21. Partially because a couple weeks before I had just broken up with someone I had really wanted things to work out with. Partially because I had known you for 6 years, and I never really saw it coming. To say timing was off was more than a bit of an understatement.

We went for it anyway. I wasn't really certain if we were going anywhere, but all I knew is you were here, you were looking at me in a way I hadn't been looked at in a long time, and that despite my reservations I had feelings for you too. Yet of course, sometimes things like to get in the way. Fear and pasts and ghosts, and I had enough for the both of us, though you had your own to deal with too. So when we called it off, when we put the brakes on it because I asked you to, it felt like a situation where better timing could've simply fixed everything. "If he were a few years older, if I had known him before, If I wasn't so broken…"

Our bad timing didn't stop there, though. You saw me and someone else together not long after we called things off and assumed that they were the reason I had left, that I didn't need time as much a replacement. We didn't speak for six months, both of us angry over miscommunications. Both of not saying what we really wanted to say.

After all of that, it seemed impossible that we could have a comeback. I was certain that any chance of an "us" was gone, and I once again turned to time to take the blame. I believed that after all of the things we had done wrong, after all the times we spoke before we thought things through and jumped when we should have waited that we had gone too far.

Yet it was you who reached out again.

Six months without us in each other's lives and finally one of us broke. You said you could live without a lot of things, but not without your best friend. Not without me. You told me you just wanted to be back in each other's lives again, not trying to push us to be anything more. This time I was upfront—that I needed to work on me before I could think about us. So we spent an entire summer taking things slowly, you standing in the background and letting me fight my demons and my battles for myself, but I always knew if I needed you then you wouldn't hesitate to stand with me. It was your encouragement and friendship during that time that made me realize just how wonderful you really were. That despite all odds and all our issues with timing, here we were. We had faced so many obstacles, we had walked away, and we found our way back to each other.

I realized that timing is a real thing. Timing is something that plays a role in our lives and our relationships. Yet if two people honestly want to work something out, then no amount of bad timing can truly destroy it.

You were the one to show me that, because when it was all said and done, it wasn't timing that destroyed us. If we had really wanted to make it work, we would've fought to find a way.

Instead, we just stopped fighting.

50

Wedding Talks with You

Baby, why did we talk
About weddings
And honeymoons
When you ended up
Leaving so soon?

Small ceremony
In our hometown
I would walk down
The aisle to
"Walk Towards Love"

Tattoos of
Sound waves
Saying
"I do."

You wanted to choreograph
A dance together
Despite that I have
Two left feet.

Now, all I can think of is
How often people say all the time
"I married my best friend."
But I don't.

I wish I was saying I do,
Instead of I don't.

51

Breakup

I'll be honest when I say I didn't see it coming.

I've always been an optimist. I've always believed that if you just hold on a little longer and try a little harder that almost anything can be fixed. You have always leaned more to realism and borderline pessimism. You are always able to see how things can go wrong long before they show up.

We both could see how different we were, that was evident from the very beginning. As time went on, though, our differences were becoming more apparent. We disagreed on things, but we always worked them out. You pushed my buttons in ways no one else ever had, and I did the same to you. We always were able to see when things weren't always wonderful, but we found ways to work around them. To me, with every new thing we faced and overcame together, I felt more confident that we were going to make it. You and me, two of the last people anyone expected to end up together, were going to take on the world hand in hand.

I guess I've always let my ideas run away with me, haven't I?

So it felt like a slap in the face when you told me you didn't see us working out long term. That you didn't see us really making a life together work. You agreed that we always worked things out, but that in all reality all of these disagreements appeared because you and I were just really different people. That when it came to a life together, we couldn't just keep temporarily fixing things, but that one—or even both—of us would have to alter themselves far too much in order to fit with the other.

The hardest part for me to face was that you were right. I couldn't deny it. I had just thought that maybe, just maybe, we would find a solution in time. That you and I would always find a way, find reasons to stay.

It turns out we did find a way, I guess. We just found out that the way was for us to go in different ones.

52

I Still Have to Wonder

You said,
"I'm just not that kind of guy;
I don't think about those kinds
of things."

I understand.
I can accept it,
Some guys just aren't great with
Words,
Affection,
and Adoration.

Little do you know I still have
the pages long texts saved,
those millennial love letters
from summers and autumns
where you swore it was the easiest thing
in the world.

Where you overwhelmed me with
Adoration,
Affection,
and Words.

And I want to ask you,

"If you aren't that kind of guy,
then who was he?"

53

I Miss You in the Little Things

The hardest part of ending a relationship
Isn't always in the big ways.
It's the little things that eat away at you.

Waking up expecting to see
"Good Morning"
and staring at a blank screen.

Listening to a song that you both loved
and knowing that you won't
hear their voice singing along beside you.

Driving down a road
and seeing a car that looks
just like theirs,
and realizing you don't have any idea
what they will be doing today.

It's the little pieces that used to tell you
"You're important to me…"
"I'm excited to tell you…"
"This was how my day was…"

All those little pieces leave empty spaces,

and as winds of change blow through these new openings
you try to muster up enough resolve
to pretend that these little things
weren't your favorite things
to look forward to.

54

Enough

I think one of the most tragic things you can learn is that two people can fight for each other, want the best for each other, and love each other to a crazy degree, and things still fall apart.

Sometimes, love just isn't enough.

Love is important and absolutely necessary, but it's not always what makes everything last. Because sometimes you can love a person for who they are, but still know that you won't last forever. You see that staying together will cause one or the other to bend and change, not in traditional compromise, but in entirely altering ways of being. You can be two strong, independent people who are proud of themselves only to discover that who you both are won't be able to finish this race together.

It's incredibly tragic, because it isn't as if the love disappeared. It's still there, beating in each other's hearts and pushing underneath your skin, screaming for an embrace or a chance to make sure this is the way things have to be.

Yet you know. You hate everything about it, because isn't it unfair? For two people to love each other only to see it won't work? Why would life bring two people together, allow them to fall for each other, and then watch as they realize that they won't end up being each other's forever? I still don't truly have all the answers, but I know that maybe somehow you need to know that love doesn't always win.

Sometimes love decides to express itself differently. Sometimes love is saying, "I can see right now that I'm not right for you, and I need to let you go to find someone else." Sometimes it says, "I can see our paths are going in two different directions, and I don't want you to leave where you are to follow me." Sometimes love proves itself by admitting when it can't offer you the things it knows you need anymore.

So maybe in the long run, love did win somehow. Because I don't know anyone who loved me quite like you, or loved me enough to look at me and see someone wonderful and full of magic and realize that I didn't need to become anything or anyone different to fit with you. You recognized that who I am is valuable and incredible, and that I would have to bend or you would have to bend for us to be in each other's lives.

I think maybe in the end you proved you loved me more than anyone else has, even if you did it by walking away.

55

Safe

I think the most difficult part
Of accepting that you didn't think
we would make it,
was that just a week before,
I had finally reached the point
believing we honestly would.

Me, the girl who was scared of this,
Me, the one who pushed you away
time after time after time,
changed her mind after almost
a whole year.

Because in a car driving home
after a long week of hectic schedules
and tense conversations,
after words flying out after misunderstandings,
I break down in the passenger seat,
apologizing for my own tears
that I can't control, that fall
without my permission.

I feel the car slow down,
and pull to the side of the road,
and all I think is,

"Did the car break down too?"
but instead I feel your arms wrap
around me and pull me to you,
letting my tears stain your shirt,
while you whisper
"It's okay, I love you."

You held onto me until I stopped,
until my cheeks were no longer covered
in salt and embarrassment.
You pulled back onto the highway,
and all I could do was think,
"He's your safe place,
he's the place you will run to,
and you know everything will be okay."

I wish I would've known that you
didn't think you could be that place for me.
I wish I could stop drowning in what used to be.
because now I'm breaking down a second time,
you're not here to hold onto me,
you're not here to tell me it's okay,

Where am I supposed to find
another safe place?
Because the one I found in you
has been soaked in the tears of yesterday

Where do I find another safe place
like you?

56

Different

I will tell you, part of me is disappointed. I'm disappointed that in the end, we both said, "We are just too different, it won't work in the long run."

Because I know, and you do too, that people who are different make things work all the time. People who are as different as night and day still make the decision to make things work, and it took me a long time, wrestling with my thoughts, on why you didn't think it was worth it to go the extra mile for me. For us.

I wrestled with this for so long, fighting off the inner voices saying, "You were just too much, you asked for too much." Yet I know that honestly, I didn't. At the end of the day, I know what I wanted, and so did you. You just didn't think of these things right off the bat, they weren't part of your natural thought's processes, and so you said, "I'm not right for you."

That would have been an easier pill to swallow if you hadn't fought for me so hard in the beginning. If you hadn't convinced a scared and broken girl that she should give love a second shot, that we were going to be different.

I won't blame you for everything, because I made the choice to jump. I made the choice to take this leap too. I also know in the end, you just didn't want to destroy me, to break me down again, and if you truly believed that was how this would all play out, then I will thank you for that too.

Yet you must know that one day, I'll still break when I see that you're willing to go that extra mile with someone who isn't me. In the end darling, two people can't fall in love and not break. Some cracks just form more subtly than others do. Some cracks form when you aren't thinking about them. Some cracks form when you least expect them.

Some breaks are more clean than others, but they're still a break nonetheless.

57

I Hope You Find Her, but Not Right Now

My mind tends to wander
into places it has
no business to,
no reason to.

We've only been broken up
For merely days, and I'm already
Mentally preparing myself
For you to end up in
another's arms.

I know you, darling,
and I know you aren't planning
on rushing out and finding
someone new,
Someone a little less me
and little more for you.

Yet already I'm accepting
That my arms just weren't
Your safe havens,
That no amount of stretching
This heart open would make it

Any more a place you could spend
Forever in.

I also know there are others,
Ones who weren't subtle
Even when we were holding onto
Each other,
Much less will they be
when words travels
That you're unattached from me.

I'm still having trouble
understanding you're unattached
from me.

I know they will run to you,
And darling, I know even if you
turn them away,
It won't be easy to watch your blue eyes
Focus on anyone else.
Even if just for a moment,
Even if it's just friendly,

Darling, can't you just keep looking at me?

58

Challenge

Thank you for being the iron that sharpened iron. The rock that I found support in but also the stone that lit the spark. If it wasn't for you, I don't know where I'd be.

Because as much as I just wish everyone would agree with me, I know that's just not the way the world works. People have different opinions and different views on the world, and usually I deal with those in a far away manner, simply reading things on a screen or a page, and pondering on why people thought the things and the way they did.

You changed all of that when you came into my life, you know. Anyone who knows you knows that you have no problem voicing your opinion, sometimes not thinking before you speak. You're passionate and you have a lot to say. It's something I loved about you, even when everything you said was the exact opposite of what I thought. Because I could see that you had just as much passion as I did, regardless of if and when we were on differing sides.

And I know as I grow older, I will come face to face with people who disagree with me, and furthermore may want to tear me down for the way I think and feel. Because of you I know better how to handle those situations, I know how to hold my ground in the face of someone disagreeing with me and to not allow it to affect me in such a personal way. I know better how to discuss something with someone and how to agree to disagree.

It was that same dynamic that kept me on my toes, because when we talked about the things we believed in, we were both passionate and engaged, and never bored. I think about 30 possibilities at once, and although I knew it drove you crazy, you admired that I could do that, that I could think beyond logistics into feelings and infinities.

And I appreciated that you stayed pretty grounded, that you held onto the most logical standpoints, and that when I was exhausted running through all the possibilities I could come back home to you. You were my safe place and the place that challenged me. The one who loved me when I was all over the place and the one I loved when all I wanted was for him to move.

You're the reason I grew and the reason I feel secure in the things I believe, and I don't think I will ever be able to thank you enough for that.

59

Opposites

He has road rage. He hits the steering wheel and wonders
what's wrong with them.
While I'm in the passenger seat pleading their case,
coming up with a million and one reasons why
they still deserve a license.

He's quick on his feet and I'm quick to forgive.
He's an untamed fire and I'm a simple candle on the mantle.
We both could just as easily burn a house down, if we really
wanted to.
He would just get there faster.

He knows the value of caring for yourself,
that to give to others you must first have something to give.
I have trouble not spending my energy on everyone else.
I'll rip my own lungs out if it means it'll help someone breathe.

He knows there are times to draw lines, and times to back out.
He sees things as Black and White, Day and Night.
But my lines are always drawn in pencil, easy to remove
If someone has an eraser colored Gray.

Our laughter strings in two separate melodies,
And our hands find different ways to hold on.
He pulls me close when I need an anchor,
I hold his hand when he isn't holding on to reality.

He's not my other half because I'm already whole.
He's not my missing piece because I'm not a broken puzzle.
He's not my super hero because I don't need saving.
He's doesn't complete me because I'm not hollow.

He's like a library; he's like a music store,
He's like the night sky; he's like a roadmap.
He shows me a million and one things that I didn't know I needed
That I didn't know I wanted.

I could have lived without reading his pages
Or learning the roads he takes, the songs he sings.
I could have lived without seeing the stars in his eyes.
Yet I'm grateful that I didn't have to.

<u>60</u>

Pursue

No one ever pursued me the way you did.

Sometimes I still can't wrap my head around it because I know I pushed your buttons and tested your patience. I know there were days I pushed you away and you couldn't understand why. I know there were times I would want you close and then run off because things felt too real. I know there were some days you probably wanted to give up on me.

Yet you never did.

You continued to be exactly what I needed every day. You were more than aware of my past, my scars, my shattered pieces, and it was definitely more than enough for any person to handle. If you had walked away, if you had told me it was too much I would've understood, because most days it was too much for me to handle too. That wasn't what you chose, though. You were the one encouraging me to keep going, even when you knew that letting me heal and letting me put myself back together might mean I take off without you. You told me that the most important thing was for me to be okay, and that whatever choices I made after that then you would learn to deal with. It was the most selfless thing I'd ever had someone do for me. Someone who was saying "I know this is a lot to deal with, that you could leave at any time, and that you may never end up with me, but I want you to be happy again, so I'm going to do whatever it takes to help you."

So you did just that. You kept true to your word, and when I was finally okay, when I was able to decide who I wanted to let into my heart, I had no questions on whether or not it was you. Even so, you still took the time to pursue me. You took the time to say, "This is what you deserve" and to back it up with your actions. And on the days where you fell short, your response was, "You deserve better." Yet it wasn't a prelude for you to make an exit, it wasn't an excuse to let me go, but it was your own call to step up and become what you thought I deserved.

If I'm honest, there are still days where I felt I didn't deserve you. There are still days where I think about how lucky I was to have found someone like you, and not only that, but to love someone like you. I had hoped that we both would never stop chasing each other, because I don't know who else in the world will ever hold a candle to us.

I don't know if I'll ever find someone quite like you.

61

When I Took Off the Rose Colored Glasses

In the end,
know that I realized
we were too different
and too set in who we are
and who we want to be
to have become anything
Together.

Know that I still say
I'm always in your corner
I still hope your life goes
the way you want it to,
that if you need someone,
you will still have
Me.

Know that I understand
I was searching for more
from you than you wanted to give,
and I apologize for trying
to ask so much more from
You.

In the end,
know that I will be fine.
I still hope you are part of
this life I'm building, yet
if you aren't, if you can't be,
I will understand that all
good things must come to an
End.

62

Best

I don't know if you realize how much I wish I could've been the right girl for you.

You told me that you didn't say anything when you started changing your mind about us because you knew I would try to "fix myself" to be more like what you needed. Boy, you knew me all too well. I think you know that when I love someone I'll bend over backwards to make things work out, that I'll do what I need to do to make sure they are happy.

You don't need to change. You are wonderful. You're amazing.

I knew you were right, but I really wish that who I was had been the right person for you. Because I know we both tried so hard to force two incredible energies to come together. I know we tried to fit puzzle pieces that just weren't supposed to meet, and the only way to make it work would be to cut away at ourselves. I wish there had been another way to just let us be without having to alter who we were.

Yet despite that, thank you for realizing this before we pushed too far.

I know that it was hard for you. It was hard on me too. Especially because love was still very much alive. It doesn't feel right to call something off when your hearts both still want each other. Yet you were always good at sensing storm clouds before they formed, while I always struggled to find even an ounce of sunshine. I know you didn't walk away from me on an impulse and I know you tried to find ways to get around it, but in the end you did what you knew I never would. You let go.

You told me I deserve someone better, someone who can give me the things I need. But darling, I hope you find the right person for you. I hope they love you as much as I did. I hope they find a home in your heart and make you certain that you will have a wonderful life with them. I hope she's everything, in all the ways I couldn't be, no matter how much I wanted to.

It may make my heart ache because I really wanted to be that person for you. Yet I know that I will be okay as long as you find the one that can be that.

Because I will always want the best for you. Even if the best isn't me.

63

Regret

I hope you know I don't regret a thing.

I don't regret anything about us. Was it hard? Absolutely. Were there days I was tired and wondered if this was worth it? Yes. Yet once it was over, once we decided that we were just better friends than lovers, it was tempting to wonder if this whole thing was a mistake?

No, darling, I can't say that it was.

Because let's face it: we've always been curious types. We had a connection, a strong one, and it became something more. If we had never chased it, we would've spent the rest of our lives wondering what would've happened if we gave it a shot. I know I would have.

At least now we know, that despite how much we care about each other, it wasn't meant to be forever. You still did a lot of things for me and showed me more than I anticipated and for that I don't think I could ever thank you enough.

I won't regret us because at least we stopped before we went too far. At least we had a chance at saving this friendship we built, and not many can say that.

It will be different. There is no way that it can't be. It will never be the exact same way that it once was. Because now we've learned the other's dark sides and tasted each others lips and there is no way that you can pretend you were only friends after moments like that. Honestly it will probably take awhile before I stop entirely looking at you as someone I'm in love with. A new girl will playfully touch your shoulder or laugh at your jokes and I'll be insanely jealous. You'll tell important things to your other friends long before I know about it and I'm sure I'll ache for the days that you were excited to let me know the good news first. If we do hang out I know for at least a little while I'll still have the impulse to grab your hand or kiss you when it's quiet.

It will take time and it will be hard, but we will be fine, I believe.

And I hope you know I don't regret any of it.

THIS IS

LOVING

MYSELF

64

More

Put down the phone, darling.

That's right, I said put it down. If he hasn't texted you back in an hour, or two, or three, just put it down. You are worth so much more than that.

I know in today's culture we are told it's okay if he doesn't make the first move. That it's okay if you text him first. That it's okay if you're the one always asking to make plans, that it's okay to be the one organizing the time to be together. You know what? Sometimes it is okay.

Yet if it's always you texting him first. If it's always you laying on the couch staring at your phone, hoping that the hours of space between texts means he's just busy. If it's you always making the dates and the hangouts, you should take a step back and realize you are worth more.

You are worth more than short late night texts and half interested conversations. More than vague compliments and empty promises. You are beautiful, you are incredible, and you have so much more to offer this world than wasting thoughts wondering why he isn't giving you the attention that deep down you know you deserve.

I know sometimes he texts you and it's wonderful. He has

really interesting conversations with you, compliments you, and makes you feel on top of the world. I know that when you two are together, he will kiss your forehead and tell you that you look amazing. I know that it's because of those moments, those magical moments, that you don't want to let him go.

But darling, you are worth more than a handful of magical moments amidst weeks of confusion and minimal effort.

I promise you that if you have put yourself out there, and he isn't responding much, or at all, it isn't simply because he is busy or passive. All of us have busy lives, including you, but we make time for the thing we think are important. He unfortunately doesn't see all the wonder and the magic that you hold inside of your heart, the things I know you want to show him if he would just ask.

You are worth more. Please spend your time on someone who sees that, instead of trying to get him to turn his head this way. I know it's hard and I know it hurts.

But please, know that you are worth more.

65

Falling

It's okay that you let yourself fall apart.

I know, that isn't the typical advice you would expect. I know you're reading articles and watching television shows that claim you need to keep it all together, girl. That you can't let yourself fall to pieces, because if you do then others will think you're weak. That your ex will really believe he made the right choice, because who would ever want a mess like that?

Well, darling, I know you. I know that you held yourself together for months upon months. I know you always like to try to make the best of a bad situation. You want to believe things will get better, and sometimes they do. Yet sometimes, life just falls apart. We don't get a say in how or when it happens to us. We don't always get picture perfect lives that don't split apart every now and again.

And you should know that when that happens, you have every right to fall apart. You don't need to answer to anyone. Because sometimes falling apart is the only way we cope with loss. It's the surrender and realization that something is over, and that can be too much to bear. So we fall apart, we allow all the cracks that have formed in us to finally break, and we let those pieces fall to the floor. We grieve. We feel. We let it happen.

There isn't anything wrong with it. Because when we fall apart, we have the chance to start building ourselves back again. We were never going to stay the same person. Not after something like this. So now, we gather all our broken pieces, and we fit them back in a new way. We sand off some of those rough and jagged edges, and bond them together with something strong, and we move forward. It's not ideal, I know. I know that if it were up to us, we would never fall apart in the first place.

Yet we did. We did fall apart, and we made a mess when we did it. But it's not something you need to look back on and regret, something to beat yourself up over. It's something you make the best out of.

And darling, we both know you're good at that.

66

What I Would Say to My 21-Year-Old Self

I want you to know I'm proud of you.

When is the last time someone
said that to you?
I'm not exactly sure.
I need you to know that I am, though.
I see where you've been
and how far you're coming.
I see that you did
what you needed to do
to survive.

For a long time you felt worthless.
You felt so ashamed,
like you just couldn't do anything right.
Poisonous words
that dripped from the lips
of the one you loved with everything you had,
words like "embarrassing" and "immature"
were added to the list of words
he used to describe you.
In all honesty, he moved those words
to the top of the list,

wrote them in bold letters,
dug the pen in the paper and
made the ink bleed.

You went month
after month trying to scrub
the definitions off of your skin,
these tattoos you didn't want,
didn't ask for.
You worked harder
and cried harder,
thinking maybe the
sweat or the tears would
erase the markings.

Saltwater didn't do you any favors, did it, darling?

So you decided you were tired
of being thrown in the fire,
and you walked away.
You didn't leave unscathed;
I know it's not that easy.

Yet you also knew that walking away,
though painful, was the right thing.
You stepped out of
your plan for forever
and picked a new path,
a new route to travel on.
You took a gut feeling
and ran with it,

you took a new dream
and handled it with care.
I know you're still scared.

Just know that I see you.
Know that if no one says it today,
tomorrow,
or next week,
I see where you're going
and what you can do.

I want you to know I'm proud of you.

67

Magic

I wish you would just look at yourself and realize you are wonderful.

I think part of you knows that. I see you looking in the mirror, and you're not unhappy with what you see. I see you making people laugh and listening to them when they need it, and you know these are good things. I see you doing the best in all that you do, and that you know effort is half of the battle; something to be proud of.

Yet I also know that as much as you see the good you bring, you also wonder why it's not enough.

You wonder why it's not enough to get a better job, or get better grades in college—or even why you can't seem to get yourself together enough to pursue a major. I know you wonder why you are working yourself to the maximum but it only barely covers your rent and bills, and you wonder how you feel you can do so much and it simply doesn't feel enough.

And then you wonder, above all these other things, why you aren't enough to keep him around. Why the person you are isn't appealing enough, smart enough, mature enough, or kind enough to make someone think that staying with you is the best choice they can make. You try your hardest to do everything right: You try not too care too much but show you care still, you give them space but come running if they need you, and you listen to their concerns and try to find a solution as best as you can. You can't seem to figure out what you're doing wrong, why does it seem everyone else has it together—and has someone—besides you?

I watch you search for yourself in their bones and under their skin. I watch you hang your hopes on their words, watch you dictate your value based on what rolls off of their tongue. You allow your self-worth to drain after every half hour that they don't respond. And I watch you see how pathetic you find yourself, but it doesn't stop you. It won't stop you for a very long time.

Oh darling, I wish you would stop trying to find yourself in other people. God created you in such a specific and wonderful way, you know this. Despite how you don't feel enough, you should know that you are more than enough. You are more than his words or their emotions, you are more than the weight on your scale or the things that you do. You were created for specific reasons, so of course not everyone is going to stay. Yet even more importantly, you aren't going to find yourself in all of them.

You may find similarities, and you can share those. Yet who you are won't be found in another person, because they were created in a specific and wonderful way too. They have their own strengths and weaknesses and issues. They are their own complex person, and trying to search them to find you will only result in disappointment. Can they bring things out in you? I believe so. I think it's why we choose our friends and lovers so carefully. Yet the moment we rely on them to find us, we've missed a chance to learn and grow, and instead we go on a scavenger hunt that we will never finish.

No darling, the only place you need to be searching is within you. The only person whose opinions should make or break you are yours. You are just as capable as anyone else in figuring yourself out, because you're intelligent and fast thinking, you are brave and you are kind, you're amazing in every sense of the word. I wish I could've told you that you will only figure out once you stop trying to look through stained glass eyes into souls to find pieces of you, and instead look into your own self.

That's when you'll see yourself for the magic that you are.

68

Yourself

Take a look at yourself in the mirror. Come on, do it. Take yourself in because, my God, there is no one else in the world quite like you. No one else who has your eyes and your laugh, your scars and birthmarks, indentions and bruises, your stories scattered across your skin. There is no one else in all of history who looks exactly like you or who ever will. You think you're too much or not enough, and you want to change as much as you can. Please know you're not a bad person for wanting to change things, but don't sell yourself so short. Please know that people will love you, people already do love you, exactly as you are.

Take a look at your mind. Your perspectives on the world are just as valuable as anyone else's. Your opinions and the way you think about things and see them in your own way are crucial in this world. The world doesn't need just one thinking pattern. The people in your life don't need only one point of view, but they need yours too even if it challenges them. Because how do we ever grow if we aren't pushed to rise to the occasion? Your voice and the way you take in this life you're living needs to be heard, so why do you quiet yourself? Why are you so afraid?

Take a look at your heart. Regardless of if you are full of all types of compassion and you think your it might burst, or you are more reserved with how it works, it's beautiful. We all have hearts and they all beat and thrive in their own ways. They way you choose to love and express love is important. Whether you are someone who is able to understand and value other's feelings and encourage them, or if you're able to press through and make necessary decisions in the midst of hard situations, you're necessary. You're not too overwhelming and you're not cold-hearted, because those labels are simply words attempting to define someone so undefinable as you. So why do you try to restrain your heart or wring it dry to squeeze out something more?

Take a moment to understand that not everyone is meant to love you, and that's perfectly okay. You are not a one size fits all option meant for hundreds of grasping hands searching for a quick fix. You weren't meant to stretch yourself thin to meet everyone's standards, skating on thin ice. You were meant to love and be loved, by people who recognize your worth, not someone trying to create it.

And until that time comes, learn to love yourself first. You must do this, and you must do this without hesitancy or doubt. Because how can anyone else ever see you are worth it if you keep telling them you're not? How can anyone love you if you tell them you aren't worth loving?

They can't. So please, love yourself. Love every single part and every single fabric that's woven you together. One day, you'll find someone who will step up and love you exactly as you are.

But today, right now, begin by loving yourself.

<u>69</u>

Love Yourself as Much as You Loved Them

You seem to have formed a bad habit
Of only seeing the worst in you
And the best in everyone else.

You love his laugh,
And call your own just noise.
You love his affection,
Yet call yourself suffocating.

You say he's a galaxy,
But you barely see yourself
As a star.

Yet can't you see by now?
There is magic in you, too.
Stop believing only they have
Something wonderful to give,
Stop quieting yourself as if
You should be hidden.

Stop breaking yourself down darling,
There is a whole big bad world out there
That is going to try and do that anyway.

70

Unattainable

By now you don't even think twice about it. It's just part of who you are and how you think. You pick the ones that seem close enough to touch but far enough out of your reach. Maybe he's the one everyone knows and talks about in your circle. Perhaps he's the one who you see every week in that coffee shop who makes eye contact but doesn't initiate conversation. Or it's the one who one day seems interested, but the next I nowhere to be found. You just can't seem to help yourself when it comes to these types; you want who you can't have.

You ask yourself why you choose the people who don't choose you. Or why you choose the people who choose you occasionally. You wonder why it's those people who spark your imagination and cause your heart to beat against your chest so loudly that you are terrified people will hear it. Why them?

The reason why it ends up being those people is because those people will never fully love you. That addiction is sometimes painful, but always constant. If there is one thing we value, it's something consistent and something we can rely on. These people are a sure thing—they will never give you their full love and attention. Regardless of if their behavior seems scattered and all over the map, in reality it's a consistent method that translates itself into one simple statement: They can only hurt you as much as you let them. They can only hurt you a little.

Because real love can also result in real pain. Intense, earth shattering pain. Real love means laying all the cards down on the table, betting all in. Anything else is just calling bluffs, tossing a few chips on the table and calling it good.

When you want the ones just out of reach, you have an understanding of what love truly is, but you can't seem to focus on it. It's overshadowed by the paralyzing fear that it won't last, that it may not result in something to rely on, but something that makes you wait for the other shoe to drop. Perhaps you've never had real love and it makes you nervous, or you've been hurt before and can't bear to go all in once more. This game you're playing is on a lower playing field, where you can hold onto your heart and indulge that part of you that is infatuated with romance. In addition, you're hoping that maybe, just maybe, if the one who is out of reach does take that leap of faith with you, then perhaps you'll finally muster up that courage yourself. If you are the reason a person sets aside their casual ways, if you're the reason they take steps forward, then you believe that love is worth it after all. You need proof, and an out-of-reach lover coming to you is the kind of miracle that will make you believe love is worth it.

You've convinced yourself that this is the way to live. To only take a certain set of calculated steps forward, only giving half of yourself, and imagining what it might be like if you and this person did end up making this whole thing work.

This wasn't the way it was supposed to be.

You know deep down that there is a reason people still put themselves out there even after they've been shattered. You know that people wouldn't simply put themselves through pain for no apparent reason. It's because real love is worth everything. It's worth heartache and suffering because true love also heals, also inspires, also restores. You may think the one who is out of reach may make you feel intense and wonderful, but that is no comparison to the way honest love can make you feel. There is no guarantee that you won't get hurt, but when you truly think about it, you're tearing yourself apart now.

You think that ripping your heart by yourself and only handing out certain pieces is best, because you're the one still holding your heart. You think this is the way to avoid heart break, but at the end of it all your heart is still broken—you just did it to yourself. If you're willing to take a chance and place your heart in the hands of someone else—someone that is right in front of you, someone who is within your grasp—there is a chance that it might break, but there is also a chance it might stay intact, and better yet grow.

Stop limiting yourself to the ones who are just out of reach in hopes of saving yourself. In the end, you can't do that by breaking yourself from the inside. Take that leap and I promise that even if you do fall, it's going to be worth it.

Love always is.

71

Him

Go ahead, let him stay.

Let him live in your memories. Let yourself press repeat every time it seems your life is forming without any trace of him in it. Remind yourself that at one point he was a huge part of your life. Force yourself to replay the past on a constant loop

Let him live in your eyes. Make sure that every time someone who looks remotely like him walks by that you always do a double take. Make sure you search for him in crowded rooms all of your old favorite places, or even in new places that he never made his own. Allow them to roam around for any sign of him, and feel disappointed when he's nowhere to be seen.

Let him live in your smile. Every time you find that you're laughing at something he didn't say or a story that he's not part of, stop yourself. Stop yourself from enjoying this new life you're creating, and only smile when you remember him or someone brings up his name. Allow him to be the only reason you show your teeth or let your laugh be heard.

Let him live in your heart. Allow him to continue to hold all of the love you can muster because you did for so, so long. Allow the idea that he might come back and really love you be enough to let him stay here. Let others visit every now and again but don't you dare allow them to bring boxes in. Any time someone else seems to be getting close to wanting to make a home in you, remind yourself that there is only room for one and you've made your choice.

Go ahead, let him stay. Allow the one who isn't even part of your life anymore hold onto all of the best parts of you. Allow your light to be hidden from the entire world because you're still trying to shine for him. Allow him to stay in places he left behind and allow him to be the most important person in your mind long after he's walked away.

Or you could let him go.

In fact, ask him to leave. Pack up your memories and your backstories and put them away. Let your eyes look for new faces, or better yet, let them look at you. Let them take you in and the person you are without his ghosts living in you. Let your smile grow so wide that your face begins to ache, but not because he isn't the source. Take time to let your heart get used to a life without someone living in it, and let it become something beautiful all on it's own. Then when the time comes, allow someone else to move in instead. Allow them to come in and make your heart their home; watch as they take care of it in ways he never did.

Because honestly, darling, the only thing that has been keeping you from being without him and moving on to better things is you. It's about time you realized he's not coming back, and honestly, you deserve better. You deserve to build an entire world that he's no longer involved in, and to make something incredible happen in it.

Please, don't let him take all the best parts of you. Take them back. Please, darling, take them back.

72

Things I Wish I Knew When Pain Became a Roommate Instead of a Houseguest

Let me tell you darling
That when you feel completely broken
Shattered, and torn apart,
When it's all just too much
Too overwhelming

Learn how to take the pain;
Swallow that bittersweet sorrow
In pieces
Bit by bit.

Because if you consume it first,
Then it can't consume you.

73

Forgiveness

I wish I could tell you that forgiveness comes easily.

I wish I could tell you that this bitterness that shackles itself around your heart, this ice that seems to try and fill the cracks formed by another's hands, will simply vanish at the magic word: Forgive.

Yet it doesn't.

Because for a long time, bitterness and sorrow are your companions. They keep you company on the dark nights when you feel lonely. They understand you in a way no one else does. Only they feel to the full extent of what you experienced—they were formed from it. Despite how bad they may be, you still choose to keep them around awhile, because don't you deserve it? Don't you deserve to feel this way after what you've been through?

Eventually though, you reach a point where you have a divide. You must choose between hurt or healing. You must choose between bitterness and forgiveness. Sometimes it isn't such a simple choice. On the one hand, you'd love nothing more than to stop feeling this way. You want to stop holding this weight of misery and you want to take steps in the direction you need to go. On the other hand, the idea of letting these people off of the hook—the ones who hurt you and tore you apart, the ones who led you on and then left, the ones who said, "I love you" and then proved to you they honestly didn't. The idea of forgiving these people seems ridiculous at best. How can you possibly allow that?

Because forgiveness isn't about them. It's about you.

I hate to say this, but they aren't going to suffer forever. After time has passed, they will move on with their lives. Regardless of which path you take in that fork in the road, chances are they have already traveled their own path awhile ago. Unless you intentionally try to make them miserable—and come on, we both know you're better than that—then they won't suffer for as long as you have been.

They will move on, and without forgiveness, you never will. That's the real tragedy here, darling. The idea that you won't be able to move forward unless you can let go of that past hurt and say, "This was terrible, but I forgive them." The idea that you would still allow these people to live inside your mind long after they have left your life. You don't deserve that. You deserve so much more.

Yet the only person who has the power to do anything about it, is you.

74

Feelings

Just because someone makes you feel a certain way, doesn't mean they are right for you.

Feelings are as tricky as they are magical. They can make you feel like you're going a million miles an hour, standing on top of the highest mountain, in an ever perpetual state of happiness. Feelings—especially brand new ones—demand to be felt, demand to be noticed. They don't allow you to just calm your way through them. They attempt to shake you up and make your heart beat faster. And when something like that happens to you, it's easy to think, "Maybe this is right. Maybe this is good."

Let me tell you, feelings don't always select their candidates well. They don't always scan and find the right guys or the best guys, despite how wonderful that would be. Feelings take a small amount of information and run with it. You create your own idea of this person in your mind until you gather more facts about them to build on. They can build into something so strong and overwhelming that it becomes easy to think, *How is this not something I should go after?*

I know it doesn't make sense, but darling sometimes you should just leave it alone.

Why? Why on earth should you pass up an opportunity to

leap at the first sign of excitement and feelings and something new? Isn't this what we live for? Isn't this the kind of things we say we need? Possibly. Yet sometimes, those feelings blind you to what is real, blind you to where you're going. You can start off thinking you'll only go so far, only walk so long down the path, only get so deep in the water. Yet before you know it you're lost, you're drowning, and you don't know how you got here.

Sometimes the way you feel about a person doesn't mean they are the right people. It means they have qualities that you like. They are what you're attracted to. You can learn from the people that make you feel intensely, but sometimes I wonder if we ever consider that we are simply supposed to let them teach us, but not consume us? What if this person shows you a side of yourself that you didn't know before? What if that person can do that without being someone you allow yourself to be swept up in? I think we would be surprised at how often we mistake a feeling for a sign—a sign pointing to someone we're supposed to end up with. Feelings are confusing and complicated, so of course we don't always know why they appear in the first place.

Yet I wish you could see that some of these people, they aren't the ones you're supposed to love. They're the ones you were supposed to learn from. They may have made you feel all sorts of things that didn't make sense, that felt powerful and intense, and maybe it just felt right to take a leap and try something with them.

Yet in the end the feelings went away, just like they did.

In the end, feelings will always subside, and you'll be left wondering how you ended up where you are. Only too late do you come to the conclusion that these weren't people you were meant to spend forever with. I wish I could say to you every time those feelings swell up inside of you that you need to slow down, take a breath, and think this through. Yet if we're honest darling, that just isn't who you are. It never has been. I can only hope that eventually you will stop chasing feelings and start chasing real things, the things that will still be here down the road instead of disappearing like fog. I hope if nothing else, you will manage to learn something out of all of this.

I hope you remember that feelings aren't all there is in this life.

75

What I Would Say to My 22-Year-Old Self

I know you tend to recognize
The importance of
Forgiveness.

I know that you look at them
and even when it's hard
You find a way to
Forgive and move on,
Forget and stay strong.

So why is it so hard
To forgive you?

Why is it that when
You remember your own
Mistakes they drag back
So much shame
That you just can't
Seem to cut yourself a break.

You carry all the past
On two bony shoulders
And tell yourself this is fine
This is the only option,

Because you brought this
On yourself.

You let everyone else go,
And you still hold onto a past you,
And say she still must make her payments
Two, three, four years later.

You didn't know, darling,
You just didn't know.
Now you do.

Would you look back
And realize you know more now
Than you did back then?
Would you look back
and realize that you can't change
who you were back then?
Won't you finally forgive yourself for your own sins?

76

Love

Oh darling, please allow yourself to love again.

I know it's terrifying. I know that in your head all you can see are the ways it can go wrong. How it will go wrong. I understand that you've already done this whole "love" thing, and it left you shattered and so scattered in the wake that you just can't imagine going through it again. You don't want to get your hopes up because you don't want to be let down again. I've been there, so believe me that when I say this it's not because I think you should just get over it and move on. I'm saying it because love is the best possible thing we possess in our lives, and it would be tragic for you to never open yourself up again.

I know you're not ready right now, and that's okay. You need to heal, and you need to relearn how to love again. Yet love isn't simply restrained to romantic partners. In fact, I think the only way you can ever truly learn to love someone again is to look around at all the types of love surrounding you now.

Once you finally start to grasp the different types of love flowing all around you, you begin to realize just how much love is truly worth it in the end. You realize that even now, you already love and are loved by people. You're afraid of something that is already threading its way through your life even if it's in the subtlest of ways. I know that romantic love seems different from the kind of love you have with others, but when you really look at it, it's not that much different at all.

Look around you. You have friends who are there for you every day and love you regardless of if you're in your best clothes or in your sweatpants with those three holes in it. Their love is consistent, and they are there when you need a shoulder to cry on as well as someone to laugh with. Learn to love them in the ways they love you—in the ways they love your mind and your personality, not your body. When you learn to love people who love your mind, you learn to love the way you think and experience things too.

You also have family, who love you so unconditionally you can't understand it sometimes. They love you despite every crazy, ridiculous, and oftentimes stupid thing you do. Even when you're in the wrong, they still love you at the end of it all. Learn to accept that love because once you realize that someone is capable of loving you despite all of your flaws, you start to understand that the ones before who walked away didn't truly love you.

And then, you have yourself. Look at yourself, darling, I know that you are your own worst critic. You know every good and bad thing about you better than most. Yet look at all you've done in your life, and you're still here. You survived and lived another day. You know there are good things that you bring to this world—you exist in this world and it's better because you're in it. When you love yourself and the strength you possess in that lion heart of yours, you begin to see the worth you've held all along that others tried to take from you.

Love is the thing we live for, die for, and fight for. We can't always explain it, and we aren't always good at it, but we crave it none the less. We were made to love and be loved. Don't let the one who broke you keep you broken. Because one day, you will find someone who is worth all the love you can give. Not the guy who can't handle you. Not the one who only wants to see you on weekends. Not the one who tries to strip down all the things that make you who you are and replace them with things they like better.

No. The one who deserves your love might be overwhelmed by you, but they stay because they are equally capti-vated—they love your mind and the way your brain works, regardless of the way you look that day. They still want you, even when you're in the wrong and have done something regretful. They see you exactly the way you are and want it all, not just the parts they pick and choose; They see your worth and appreciate it.

Because that's what honest love is. And it's nothing you should be afraid of.

77

What I Would Say to My 23-Year-Old Self

Maybe when it's all said and done,
We cross a few people in our lives
That make us feel and live and move
Beyond any possible thing
we could comprehend.
People we love without
hesitation and believe in
without boundaries.

Maybe we forget
one of those people
is supposed to be
our own self.

78

Remember

I know that right now, it's painful.

I know that it might still hurt you when you hear their favorite song on the radio, causing you to flashback to their ridiculous dance moves in the car. Or sitting down in their preferred place to eat and remembering how their eyes used to glance up from the table to meet yours, causing you to blush. Or you smell the cologne they used to wear, and recall how it felt to be wrapped in their arms, or your head on their shoulder, feeling like this was home.

Those memories might still hit you like a ton of bricks and all you want to do is forget, forget, forget. Because remembering means pain, remembering means being forced to recognize what you lost and how you had them one day and then they were gone the next.

You wish you could just rip them out of your memories. Go under a knife and have them cut away every last smile, quote, and picture from your mind. If you could just go back and act like you never knew them, then they could never hurt you. A person you never knew can't hurt you can't leave you behind.

I can't honestly tell you that tomorrow will be so much better. I can't say that it won't take a long time to heal. I can't pretend that you will wake up one day and forget he ever existed.

Here is what I can promise you. Things will get better.

Maybe they get worse before they do; maybe everything will overwhelm you and you just aren't sure that you can breathe, much less live. You won't stay that way, though; eventually things do start to get better. Maybe it happens all at once, or it happens in little pieces, in every morning that you wake up and do something for you. In every time that you take a step in a new path, or laugh at something hilarious, or go out of your way to smile at someone new. Yet things do get better. The ache does ease; the hurt does fade. You will pick up your broken pieces and find some way to make them work together again. You will heal and you will manage to close all the doors that their ghost used to keep their foot in.

And one day, you'll skim through the radio stations, when their favorite song will play. Or you'll sit down in that preferred restaurant and order a meal. Or you'll inhale that familiar scent that you used to crave, that used to be them.

You'll remember, but it won't crush you. You'll see them as someone who at one time brought you happiness and laughter. A small part of you might feel a tinge of sadness, but you'll look back with a smile, see their face pop up in your mind, and you'll remember that what you had was good. It was real. It was memorable.

And you'll be so grateful that you didn't forget.

79

Kaitlin's Words on Why Love Hasn't Lasted for Me Yet

She says,
"Love isn't supposed
to be this hard.
You make things too hard."

It's true, sweet girl.
You have a lot of love,
and you'll use every last drop
on anyone who you believe
might love you too.

I think you've loved the challenge
more than you've loved love.
I think you fall
for puzzles and riddles,
complexities that you
have to unravel.

You have a heart
big enough to swallow
all the imperfections and difficulties.
You wear rose-colored glasses

197

even when it's storming,
even when the darkness falls.

She tells me,
"I think love will find you,
it will sneak up on you when
you can't see it coming,
and it won't be this hard,
it will just,
be."

80

Whole

There will come a day, where you will realize that the person you are, and the person you're becoming doesn't need another person beside you to be whole.

You will stand firmly on your own two feet and realize that you've been capable of taking on the world this whole time without someone reassuring you that you can do it.

You will look into your own reflection, every part of you, and believe that yes, you are beautiful and attractive, without another voice in your ear telling you this truth that you've discovered all on your own.

You will hear your own voice speak out opinions and engage in conversations, and will be captivated by your own mind and how it works. You will take those thoughts and ideas and do something incredible without someone telling you how intelligent and driven you are.

You will chase dreams and passions that your heart will scream out for, you will run down paths without warning and succeed in things you love beyond your wildest expectations. Yet you'll be so proud of yourself because you won't constantly be looking back to see if someone is behind you—because you are enough.

At the end of the day darling, you are enough. You always have been. It may have taken you awhile to see that and to finally reach this place, but you have *always been enough.*

Congratulations, you're finally experiencing the kind of love you've been trying to get from everyone else, and it turns out you've had it in you all along.

About the Author

Lacey is a 23-year-old writer and poet from Owensboro, Kentucky who is also studying Youth Ministry at Evangel University. She loves coffee, puppies, Myers-Briggs, naps, Taco Bell, making people happy, and having heart-to-hearts involving all of the feels.

Thought Catalog, it's a website.
www.thoughtcatalog.com

Social
facebook.com/thoughtcatalog
twitter.com/thoughtcatalog
tumblr.com/thoughtcatalog
instagram.com/thoughtcatalog

Corporate
www.thought.is

Made in the USA
Middletown, DE
01 June 2022